THE LIFE AND TIMES
OF THE BEATLES:
The Spurious Chronicle
of Their Rise to Stardom,
Their Triumphs & Disasters,
Plus the Amazing Story
of Their Ultimate
Reunion

A Novel by Mark Shipper

Fred Jordan Books/Sunridge Press
A DIVISION OF GROSSET & DUNLAP, INC., NEW YORK

Fred Jordan Books/Sunridge Press

A DIVISION OF GROSSET & DUNLAP, INC.
1120 Avenue of the Americas, New York, N.Y. 10036

First Printing 1978

Printed in U.S.A.

TO GEORGEANN

In an exclusive interview for this book,
Ringo Starr tells the entire Beatles' story to author
Mark Shipper (right). Shipper then proceeds
to lose his notes on the way home, which forces him
to make up his own version of their story.

Author's Note

Paperback Writer is a work of semifiction. It is a novel with one foot in reality, yet most of the events described herein and the accompanying illustrations existed solely in my imagination. All of the direct quotations are purely fictitious.

—M. S.

Contents

Foreword

Rock & roll is a joke
and the joke is on
anyone—performer or
audience—who ever takes
it for any more than that . . .

That line appeared in the first essay I ever wrote about rock music, seven years ago. It seemed then—as it does today, even more than ever—to be the only sane way to view the subject.

This may be an irreverent attitude, may even convey a lack of respect for the music and its fans.

I certainly hope so.

Rock & roll—from Little Richard and Jerry Lee Lewis to the Beatles and Stones and Led Zeppelin, right on up to today's "new wave" music—has always been fundamentally rooted in irreverence and disrespect.

It is a joke! But it's the greatest, funniest, longest-lasting joke of all time. Rock & roll music began and continues to be little but loud, dumb, silly, vulgar, attention-getting, adolescent noise. It speaks directly to the kid in all of us, and it keeps him—and through him, us—young, vital, and immunized against the pretensions that constantly threaten to turn us into lifeless, joyless, serious, boring people. *Paperback Writer* is a rock & roll novel.

If there were a way to play this book on your record player, I would hope that it might sound something like "Be My Baby," or "Fun Fun Fun," or "Twist and Shout," or . . . well, you get the idea.

I'm aiming this book directly at the kid in you. If you love rock & roll, he'll be easy to find. And if the kid in you is asleep, don't you think it's about time you woke him up?

—Mark Shipper
Los Angeles, California
February 1978

1

Come Together

LOS ANGELES, CALIFORNIA, December 7, 1979—
Everyone knew it would happen. Knew the Beatles would
eventually get back together, cut another album, go on
tour again. At least now that their long-awaited reunion is
a part of history everyone *says* they knew. The more
brazen even pretend they realized all along how it would
happen: how the reunion would be received, what the
reaction of the fans and the media would be, even how the
Beatles themselves—John, Paul, George, and Ringo—would
feel about it all.

But the fact is, there was no way anyone could know
what would happen. We were all too affected by their
impact to clearly foresee the logical conclusion of such a
series of events. We weren't serious students of the
Beatles. We were fans. Plain and simple. Fans. We were
all so caught up in their magical mystique that we seldom
looked beyond it; and even when we did, what we saw was
so confused and tangled, so fantastic and complex, that it
would have been impossible to predict the strange twists
the Beatles story would take. But their story had always
been an amazing and unpredictable one.

Right from the start, the Beatles were an unlikely mix.
Back in 1961 in Liverpool, England, young John Lennon
and Paul McCartney wanted no part of each other. On
one side stood Lennon, heading up an exciting and hard-
driving rock band, the Beatles, whose members included
George Harrison, Pete Best, and Stuart Sutcliffe. On the

other, McCartney, a childhood chum of the Beatles who had already begun a highly promising solo career and had established a sizable following throughout Liverpool and its surrounding regions.

The Beatles, talented as they were, enjoyed little success in those days and their prospects for a future in the pop world seemed slim. Observers recall that what seemed to be lacking was a focus, a pretty face for the teenage girls to latch onto. The British music scene was then dominated by such pop idols as Billy Fury, Cliff Richard, and Tommy Quickly. A tough, uncompromising rock & roll outfit simply couldn't endure in such a bland environment.

Harrison, Sutcliffe, and Best were growing impatient with the lack of jobs and the poverty-level wages the Beatles were earning. They suggested that Lennon approach McCartney and offer him a role in the group. Lennon wanted no part of it.

"We're a *rock* band. What'll we do with that wimp?" friends recall him saying at the time. But the others persisted. Finally, they threatened to quit. Lennon had no choice.

"What makes you think he'll even be interested?" he asked. "He's already got an album out, he gets his pictures in the magazines, he's making money."

"At least we can try, John," Harrison said. "Deep down, Paul's a rocker. I can't believe he's happy with that crap he's putting out."

At first, McCartney was reluctant, but he told Lennon that he'd think it over. "Me join that seedy bunch of Teddy boys? I'd have to be crazy," he told friends the next day. But privately he deeply admired the Beatles. And Harrison was correct—McCartney did hate the polite, sterile music he was forced to perform onstage. It took him a week, but he made his decision: he was joining the Beatles. His friends, family, and especially his management, were shocked and outraged. How could he turn his

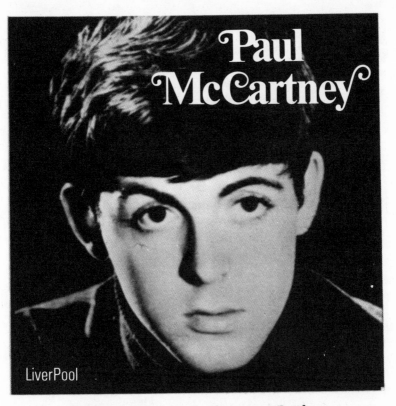

Paul McCartney's extremely rare pre-Beatle
solo album on the local Liverpool Records label.
Original copies have sold for more than
$2000 in Beatle collectors' auctions.

back on almost-certain stardom? And to throw it away to join that pack of Teds who were going nowhere? They'll just use you, Paul, they told him, to get better jobs and a few more pounds in their pockets, and all of you will be finished in two years' time. You'll see.

Their skepticism only firmed McCartney's resolve to join up with Lennon and Company. He finished two weeks of live appearances that were already booked for him, then headed off to Hamburg, Germany, where the Beatles were working the now-famous Star Club.

It was an intense time for the Beatles. They worked seven nights a week, eight to ten hours per night, for the rowdiest, toughest audience in all of Europe. They lived in the club, upstairs, all four sharing one room and one bathroom. Afternoons were spent rehearsing material to get them through the upcoming evening. Hans Däun, bartender at the Star Club in the early sixties, recalls the afternoon McCartney arrived at the club for the first time:

Sind Sie sich darüber im Klaren, dass, wenn Ihnen dies hier wirklich verständlich ist, Sie zu den Eingeweihten gehören, die vielleicht nur 1 Prozent der gesamten Weltbevölkerung ausmachen? Denn in diesem deutschen Absatz werden wir Ihnen nichts über Paul McCartney mitteilen. Wir werden Ihnen auch nichts über John Lennon, Pete Best, George Harrison oder Burt Reynolds erzählen. Weshalb? Weil Reynolds gar nichts mit den Beatles zu tun hat! Wenn Sie gescheit genug sind, diesen Absatz zu verstehen, sollten Sie auch nicht eine so offensichtlich idiotische Frage stellen. Da Sie jedoch zu den Auserwählten gehören, wollen wir Ihnen ein Geheimnis verraten, das wir den nicht deutsch-lesenden Angehörigen des Publikums vorenthalten: trotz allem, das Sie später lesen werden, ist der Verfasser in der Wirklichkeit einer der begeistertsten Anhänger George Harrisons in der Welt. Ja, das ist wirklich wahr. Nur die Tatsache, dass dieser Absatz von Paul McCartney handeln soll, hält uns davon ab, über George zu schreiben, anstatt dauernd McCartney zu erwähnen. Aber wir müssen McCartney dauernd erwähnen, damit das Wort "McCartney" immer wieder aus dem deutschen Text hervorspringt und dadurch diese ganze Geschichte glaubwürdig erscheint. Es ist nett, dass Sie mitmachen und vergessen Sie in Ihrem Weg durchs Leben diese beiden Worte nicht: Paul McCartney. (Und somit nehmen wir unser termingemässes Buch, dass sich bereits im Gange befindet, wieder auf.)

Hans' observations were confirmed by an American waiter, Marc Kerner, who also worked at the club at the time:

I remember it like it was yesterday. The boys were sitting around the empty club, drinking beer and chatting to the waitresses who were busy setting up the club for that evening. They were dressed in the only clothing I ever saw them wear in Germany— black leather jackets, T-shirts, and faded blue levis. All of a sudden, in walks this freshly scrubbed, good-looking chap in an expensive tailored French suit. Stuck out like a rose in a thatch of weeds. The others crowded around him and told him right off that the suit had to go. He surprised them then. Opened up his suitcase and showed them a brand-new, shiny leather jacket, a black T-shirt, and a pair of levis, well-worn and with blue paint splotched throughout. I can still remember the five of them rehearsing that afternoon. Four scruffy Teds and this new kid in his suit, playing piano. Stu Sutcliffe was handling the bass guitar in those days. Everyone was amazed at McCartney's ability. He not only knew how to play all the songs they'd been doing, he knew the words to every one and sang like a young Little Richard. He'd done his homework, all right. I feel fortunate that I was able to witness the show that night. To my mind, they never equalled the excitement and energy they put into that performance. Finally, everything had clicked into place. I knew then that it was only a matter of time before they would be world-famous. And I was right . . .

With the experience gained in Hamburg, the Beatles returned to Liverpool as a group to be reckoned with. They accepted a job as house band at a small, grimy, underground club called The Cavern, and built a following that soon was to encompass virtually every young person in the city. The group had cemented itself at four members: Lennon on rhythm guitar and harmonica, Harrison on lead guitar, Pete Best on drums, and McCartney on bass guitar. (Stuart Sutcliffe, the fifth Beatle, had fallen in love with a German girl and stayed behind in Hamburg. He died a few months later.)

Even with all their local fame, they might never have gotten out of Liverpool if a young plumber named Brian Epstein hadn't been called to The Cavern one night to repair a clogged pipe in the ladies' restroom. Epstein, like all plumbers, was financially secure, and more than a little bored with the occupation of plumbing. That, coupled with the fact that plumbing was not considered a proper way for a young Jewish man to earn a living, was a constant source of discontent for Epstein.

Epstein, tools in hand, walked into the club that fateful November night in 1961 thinking only of the time-and-a-half he would be able to charge for the emergency job, not knowing that the scene that followed would permanently alter his life.

He pushed his way through the frenzied crowd of

Beatles fans until he found the bathroom. Over the deafening noise, Epstein shouted through the bathroom door: *"Plumber here! Is anybody in there? I have to get in!"*

He waited, heard nothing but the booming music, and entered. To his surprise, the bathroom was not only occupied, it was packed with teenage girls. Because of the noise, they hadn't heard his warning. Epstein froze. He wanted to run, to get out. But he couldn't move. His face turned several colors, finally stopping at white. A 200-pound girl shouted at him from a toilet stall. Epstein was still paralyzed. He turned his head away, but it got worse. Before him stood three teenage girls slouched against a sink. The oldest couldn't have been a day over sixteen. The others were younger. Fourteen years old, maybe. The two fourteen-year-olds were in the process of helping the older one find a vein in her left arm that was still able to accommodate the hypodermic needle that one of them was holding. When the girls spotted Epstein, they screamed *"Police!"* at the top of their lungs. Another girl suddenly appeared out of nowhere with a knife. She was headed straight for Epstein. His survival instinct finally broke through his paralysis, enabling him to burst out the door back into the nightclub.

Dazed, his heart pounding, he leaned against the back wall of The Cavern. God, the noise! It was intolerable. And, yet, it appeared these kids couldn't get enough of it. An idea struck him: a man could make a sizable bit of money with a piece of this action. He decided to wait around for the show to end, knowing now he could never go back to plumbing. Not after *that* incident.

Epstein wasn't the only one who wanted to get backstage after the show. There were dozens of girls pressed against the door, waiting for their heroes to emerge. The club's bouncer held them back. Epstein, his tool kit still in hand, managed to convince the bouncer that there was a leak in the dressing room, and gained entry.

The Beatles were in the process of finishing off a couple pints of beer when Epstein walked in. He inquired as to whether they had a manager. When they told him they didn't, he went to work. Liverpool was too small to contain their talent, he told them. With a sound like theirs, they could change the world. They could become richer than their wildest dreams. They could perform benefits for impoverished countries. The world could be theirs!

The Beatles were interested, but cautious, particularly John Lennon.

"What makes you think you can do all that for us?" he asked.

"I've got connections, I've got business know-how. I've got salesmanship abilities like nobody's ever seen," Epstein replied.

"Come off it," Lennon said. "If you're such hot stuff, why are you only a plumber?"

"A plumber? He's a plumber?" McCartney said, surprised.

"Sure he is. Ever see a businessman carry around a toolbox full of pliers, spanners, and wrenches?"

Epstein had been found out. He was looking for a comfortable way out when George Harrison came to his rescue.

"Plumbers make a lot of money, John," he said. "Nobody's got more money than plumbers. You got a lot of money, Epstein?"

"More than I know what to do with," Epstein replied. "First thing I'll do is buy the lot of you brand-new equipment."

They perked up. Epstein could feel a change.

"Then I'll set you all up in clean flats, with hot and cold water and fresh towels and TV sets."

John Lennon onstage in Hamburg, 1962.

"I like it, John," George said. "I'm tired of living in slime. I want to take a shower every day. Cleanliness is next to Godliness.[1] And we do need new equipment; there's no denying that."

Lennon was ready, too, but figured he'd angle Epstein for as much as he could.

"My Aunt Mimi's got a clogged sink in her kitchen and the hot water runs out after three minutes in the bathroom so she can't take a decent bath. Will you fix that?"

"Tomorrow. You tell her I'll be there."

"OK with me then," Lennon said. "What about the rest of you?" He looked at the others. They nodded affirmatively. Epstein was in.

1. First recorded instance of Harrison's future religious inclination.

2

Don't Pass Me By

The first order of business for Brian Epstein (after repairing the sink and installing a new hot water heater for John's aunt) was to secure a recording contract for the group.

He brought the boys to a small studio where they made a demo tape of five songs, which he would play for the record companies. That tape went on to become a valuable collector's item. The Beatles put down elementary versions of "Roll Over Beethoven," "A Taste of Honey," "I Saw Her Standing There," "Twist and Shout," and "Happiness Is a Warm Gun."

Epstein first tried the small Liverpool label that McCartney's solo album had been released on. They weren't interested. Next he went to London, where he was met with indifference and hostility at every turn. "Rock groups are a thing of the past," he was told. "Come back when you've got a singer/songwriter or a rock opera based on the Bible. That's what the kids want today."

But Epstein refused to quit. He kept remembering that night at The Cavern. If it could happen there, it could happen anywhere: ladies' bathrooms were all over England. He had to keep going with this new project. After months of frustration, he finally got a break.

It happened like most breaks happen: by accident. It occurred to him that it would be more convenient for record companies to listen to a cassette tape, rather than the cumbersome reel-to-reel variety he was carrying around with him. He took his tape to EMI's recording studios, where he was told by a veteran recording engineer, George Martin, that cassette tape had not been invented yet. Martin suggested instead that Epstein have the tape transferred to disc, which Martin was equipped to do right on the premises that afternoon.

While transferring the tape to disc, Martin heard something, a sound like he'd never heard in his fifteen years in the business. He called Epstein into the studio.

"You hear that?" he asked Epstein.

"Hear what?"

"That sound. I've never heard anything quite like that sound, Mr. Epstein."

Epstein beamed. At last his patience was rewarded.

"It isn't tape hiss," Martin continued, "and it isn't our tape heads, either. We just had them cleaned this morning. I'm afraid there's no way I can keep that irritating noise off your disc, Mr. Epstein. I wanted you to hear it for yourself, so you'd know it wasn't our fault when you heard it on the disc."

Now Epstein, deflated and heartbroken, exploded:

"I don't give a damn about the bloody tape hiss! I thought that maybe you, a man of experience and stature in this business, might be able to tell that the music on that tape is the future of the record industry! But you're just like the rest of them, aren't you? You'll sign every bloody rock opera that comes walking through that door, but put something exciting and different in front of you, and what do your jaded ears hear? Tape hiss, that's bloody what!"

"No need to cause a scene, Epstein. You didn't say you were looking for a record contract when you came in. You just needed a disc pressed. That's all you said, remember?"

"I'm sorry. I'm sorry. I guess the frustration finally got me. You're only doing your job. It's just that I can't bear the thought of going back to plumbing."

"Tell you what, Epstein," Martin said. "You leave this

In pre-Beatlemania days, the Beatles could walk
down a London street just like anybody else.
In this 1962 photo, group goes in search of hoodlum
who cut off the end of George Harrison's
tie.

tape with me and I'll play it at the new-product meeting we're having today at four o'clock."

"Why, thank you, Mr. Martin. That's very kind of you."

"I can't promise anything, mind you, but I'll do what I can and I'll call you tonight and let you know either way."

Well, at least there's hope, Epstein thought to himself as he walked slowly out into the noonday London fog.

At 5:30 P.M. Epstein received the call he'd been waiting for.

"Good news, Mr. Epstein," said the voice at the other end. "The vote was close, but we're willing to take a chance on a 45 rpm and an album," Martin told him.

Epstein was elated. What seemed impossible only that morning was actually going to become a reality. And EMI! They don't come any bigger.

"I'm extremely grateful to you, Mr. Martin. The boys will be delighted. If there's ever any way I could repay the favor, please let me know."

"Well, there is one thing you might be able to do for me," Martin replied.

"Anything. You just name it."

"The bathtub drain at my house is clogged. Could you gather your tools and be over at, say, eight o'clock?. . ."

3

It's All Too Much

When news arrived that they'd been signed to EMI, the Beatles did two things. First, they threw a party that all Liverpool still talks about. Second, they kicked Pete Best out of the group and replaced him with one Richard Starkey [1] (aka Ringo Starr). Starr was a fairly well-known drummer on the local circuit, playing with Rory Storm & the Hurricanes when he was approached by George, John, and Paul. Rory Storm was on the downslide of a roller-coaster two-year career that saw him gain a Top Ten British single,[2] then plummet until he could barely get work anywhere in England. In a desperate attempt to regain an audience, he had taken to tawdry gimmicks, including setting up machines at the sides of the stage which blew gusts of wind on the Hurricanes while they played.

When the Beatles tracked down Ringo, he was at home, suffering the second bout of pneumonia he'd had in as many months, caused by (in his words) "Rory's god-damned wind machine. Hasn't anybody told him it rains a lot in England?" Ringo eagerly accepted the offer to join the Beatles, and three weeks later the group was travelling to London for its first recording session.

To say that the Beatles were slightly nervous on that

1. Even if there had been *two* Richard Starkeys, it's likely they would have used only one of them.
2. "Ruby Red Dress," later a U.S. hit for Helen Reddy.

September day in 1962 when they walked into EMI's recording studios would be putting it mildly. This would be the test, and they all knew it. The outcome of this day would determine whether or not they'd have a future in the British music scene.

Clutching their guitars, they were shown around the studio by George Martin. He asked them to let him know if there was anything they didn't like. In a now-famous quote that illustrates perfectly the spirit of irrepressibility which the Beatles later became identified with, George Harrison said, "For starters, I don't like your tie." Less famous is Martin's response: "If you don't like my tie, how about a daiquiri or a margarita?" [3]

The session lasted sixteen hours. From it came the Beatles' first album. It was the most productive sixteen hours in popular music history.

The album, *We're Gonna Change the Face of Pop Music Forever,* was a perfect reflection of the self-confidence and power the young Beatles exuded.

Of the fourteen songs on *We're Gonna Change the Face of Pop Music Forever,* eight were original Lennon-McCartney compositions. Although commonplace today, it was unheard of then for a British rock band to use predominantly self-penned material. The standard practice was to record "cover" versions of successful American songs which were still unknown to English audiences.

Of these eight original tunes, "Love Me Do" was chosen as the first Beatles single. To say that it received immediate universal acclaim from every sector of the nation would not only be misleading, it would be downright inaccurate. The song, a slight, harmonica-dominated tune with banal lyrics, gave no indication of what was to come from the foursome. The Beatles could consider themselves fortunate that the record climbed as high as the lower regions of the 20s on the English chart.[4]

3. Hey, he was a producer, not a comedian!
4. Many informed observers claim that even this unimpressive chart placing

THE BEATLES

WE'RE GONNA CHANGE
THE FACE OF POP MUSIC
FOREVER

THEIR FIRST ALBUM—A bold claim,
but the talent to back it up.

As a follow-up single, George Martin was intent on having the group record a song written by a then-promising newcomer named Freddy Mercury. The song, "Bohemian Rhapsody," was detested by the group, with the exception of Paul McCartney.

"You like it because it sounds like that crap you used to sing before you joined us," said John, who, owing no doubt to his own insecurity, often made McCartney feel like an outsider.

Instead, the Beatles chose their own composition, "Please Please Me," as a follow-up. By doing so, they demonstrated their remarkable grasp of the English audiences' taste. The record shot up to number one and launched the phenomenon the world came to know as "Beatlemania."

"Please Please Me" was simply an incredible record for its time. Even today it stands up as well as it did in 1963.[5] The superb construction of this song betrays an innate understanding of pop music that explains every bit of success that was to come later.

As for "Bohemian Rhapsody," it also reached number one. But not for thirteen years. Had the Beatles waited that long, it's likely that the enthusiasm which had propelled them to the top would have cooled somewhat.

---

came as a result of the rumor that when the record was played backward at 78 rpm John could be heard repeating in the background, "Paul is dead."

5. Especially when leaned up against a wall.

4

Getting Better

After "Please Please Me" came "From Me to You," another number-one song. For a group to come out of nowhere to score with a number-one song was not unheard of. In fact, for a group to come out of nowhere to score *two consecutive* number-ones was also not unheard of.[1] Even so it was quite an accomplishment, and Brian Epstein was greatly relieved that plumbing was finally a part of his past.

The Beatles played their final gig at The Cavern club in August 1963. Amazingly, it was their 294th Cavern performance.[2] During that month, the record that was most often to be associated with them, "She Loves You," was released as their new single. The song's "yeah, yeah, yeahs" instantly became a Beatles trademark.

More than a decade and a half has passed since the release of "She Loves You" and when played today it still sounds as good as it did then.[3] It climbed to number one faster than did any previous Beatles record, and the Beatles were firmly established as the top group in England. Their pictures dominated the fan magazines, and photos of their riotous concerts appeared daily in the

1. It was beginning to appear that nothing was unheard of in the British pop world. Pete Best was the exception. He was never heard of again.
2. The 294 performances in themselves were not particularly amazing. The fact that somebody was *actually counting them* was, however.
3. Providing that the record has been kept in a sleeve and protected with periodic cleaning.

newspapers. And those concerts! It was entirely possible to sit through a Beatles concert from start to finish and not hear one note of music above the ceaseless din of screaming teenage girls.

In the jargon of the music industry, the Beatles were "home." They had conquered England. It was theirs. Brian Epstein was already thinking ahead to his next conquest, a move so bold and previously unthinkable that it wasn't even discussed at the meetings that the group and management conducted every Tuesday night during this period. Brian Epstein wanted to conquer America. But he knew he couldn't do it alone. As always, he needed the Beatles.

In those days, there had been only one American hit that came from England: Frank Ifield's "I Remember You." Americans had their own pop music industry. There was competition enough at home without asking for more from a foreign country. But just as Epstein was convinced that what happened in Liverpool could happen throughout England, he believed that what had happened throughout England could happen in America.[4]

He flew to the States and arranged a meeting with Ed Sullivan, at that time the king of American TV. Sullivan was aware of the Beatles' impact in their native land, and—always on the lookout for new talent—was very much interested in having the group appear on his Sunday night show.

Epstein and Sullivan discussed the matter over a lunch that is now historic.[5] Sullivan, like any good businessman, concealed his eagerness to get the Beatles' debut American performance. He knew he could get the deal on his terms. He always had in the past, hadn't he? What he

4. As it happened, he happened to be correct.
5. So historic, in fact, that although the New York restaurant where the meeting took place has been torn down for years, the table where Epstein and Sullivan sat still remains. Visitors to New York can find the table at the end of Lane 14 at Manhattan Lanes, the bowling alley constructed on the site in 1970.

The Beatles' official photographer in the early days,
F. Stop Fitzgerald, not only recorded his
subjects on film, but on tape as well. Fitzgerald's
recording of this famous session:
"OK, Paul, put your right arm across your
waist, fold your left arm over it and tweak your chin
thoughtfully . . . John, stand sideways and I
want you to fold your arms, too . . . Ringo! Stop
falling down! . . . George, do me a favor and
hold him up, will you? Thanks . . . now just jut out
your left leg a little . . . that's perfect! OK,
now everybody look over here . . . Smile! . . ."

didn't plan for was a brash, cocky, confident Brian Epstein. Epstein knew he held the goods and wasn't willing to compromise an inch. His terms seemed outrageous at the time, and still do. First, he insisted that the Beatles get top billing.

"Top billing for an unheard-of teenage combo? Impossible." Sullivan was incredulous.

"By next year at this time, they'll be the biggest thing to ever hit show business," Epstein countered.

"Mr. Epstein, do you realize how often I hear that claim? Every day of my life, that's how often. And even if I wanted to accommodate you, how can I give top billing when I've already got Alan King booked for the same show?"

Epstein continued as though he hadn't heard a word Sullivan said.

"Not only do I want top billing, Mr. Sullivan, I want top billing on the *three consecutive weeks* the Beatles appear on your program."

Sullivan was speechless. Neither said a word for about thirty seconds. Sullivan looked into Epstein's eyes.

"You're really serious, aren't you?"

"I've never been more serious in my entire life, Mr. Sullivan."

"We've never done anything like this in the fourteen years I've had the show," Sullivan said. "I've got to think about this. I've really got to think about this."

He held his right hand in the air and snapped his fingers. Immediately, two waiters appeared. "Bring me a telephone right away," he commanded. "I've got to call my wife," he told Epstein. "She's the only person I can count on to give me a straight answer. Everybody on my staff kisses my ass."

Epstein excused himself and retreated to the men's room to afford Sullivan privacy. When he returned, Sullivan had made his decision.

"OK, Epstein," Sullivan said. "My wife thinks it's

crazy, too, but she told me something that I lose sight of sometimes. You can't afford to play it safe in this business. You've got to take a shot once in a while. You've got to trust your gut feeling. I didn't get to the top by playing it safe. If we can work out the details, you've got your three weeks. You've got your top billing, now pay the check and let's go."

"Me? I thought you were taking *me* out to lunch."

Sullivan let out a long, low sigh as he reached across the table for the check. "Anything else you want from me, Epstein? The deed to my house perhaps?"

"Well, I could use a ride back to my hotel," Epstein said, "if it's not too much trouble."

"No problem."

"Thank you, Mr. Sullivan. That's very kind of you."

"Not really," Sullivan said wearily. "After all, you just took me for quite a ride."

5

I Wanna Be Your Man

It was the classic rags-to-riches story. The Beatles—only a year before just another of the hundreds of rock & roll bands proliferating throughout England—now had a number-one single, a number-one album, and America awaiting their arrival. Certainly they were talented, but no more so than a dozen other groups on the scene. At least that's the way it looked to Mick Jagger, a young man from Richmond who was lead singer of an avant-garde R&B group, the Rolling Stones.

"We could be as big as those guys if we wanted to sell out like they did," Jagger said to his lead guitarist, Brian Jones, one night while the group was between sets at Richmond's Crawdaddy Club. The conversation was sparked when Jagger's girlfriend told him that John Lennon and Brian Epstein were in the audience. Her remarks were overheard by the emcee, Clive Ormsby, who interrupted Long John Baldry's set to announce the fact from the stage:

"Excuse me a moment, Long John. The Crawdaddy Club is pleased to announce tonight that in attendance is John Lennon of the Beatles, with his manager, Brian Epstein. Stand up and take a bow, fellows." The audience came alive with the announcement. Necks craned; young girls ran over to the table. It was five minutes before Baldry could continue. Jagger was visibly unimpressed.

"Big deal. I mean, big fucking deal," he said to Brian Jones, who nodded his head in silent agreement. "Remember last year when we caught them in Liverpool?"

Jones smiled. "Yeah. They were so lame with all that 'Please Mr. Postman' crap they were doing. Shit. We were laughing so hard."

"You know," Jagger said, "I still think they're lame." He did an ultra-nasal impression of the Beatles' first single, emphasizing the last word of each line, which made the simple lyrics sound even more banal:

". . . Luv, luv me *do*, you know I love *you*, I'll always be *true*, so ple-e-e-ease love me *do*."

Jones cracked up at Jagger's impression. So did Jagger's girlfriend, a mature-looking Oriental woman. Jagger had sold her on rhythm & blues, a music she hadn't even heard of a month before. But now she possessed the fervor of a new convert:

"Those Beatles are so silly, aren't they, Mickey? They've probably never even heard of Elmore James or Blind Lemon Jefferson."

"Take it easy, luv," Jagger cautioned her. "You never even heard of them yourself until last week."

The Stones took the stage for their next set. They opened with a searing version of Chuck Berry's "Around and Around," then launched into a primal reading of Slim Harpo's overtly sexual "I'm a King Bee." The Stones were *hot*, they lived this music and this was obvious to every member of their rapidly growing following. On this particular night, however, the response from the crowd was much less than the usual frenzy. Jagger could feel it from the stage, but he couldn't figure it out. Weren't the vocals cutting through Brian's and Keith Richard's guitars? Was Charlie [Watts, the Stones' drummer] drowning the band out? He looked at Keith imploringly, as if to ask, "What's wrong?" Richard lifted a finger off his pick in mid-chord and pointed toward a table on the right-hand side of the stage, where Lennon and Epstein sat. Then

Jagger understood. The audience was watching Lennon, watching *his* reaction to the Stones, watching *him* sip his drink, light *his* cigarette, talk to the girl sitting next to him, who Jagger recognized. It was Jagger's girlfriend! With the guy from that candy-ass pop group! The song ended. The group was all set to break into their next number, "Little Queenie," when Jagger stopped them. He was gonna show John Lennon and his prissy manager what *real* music was all about. Away from the mike, he mumbled a song title to the group. It was the nastiest song in their repertoire: "I Just Wanna Make Love to You." No double meaning in this one. He had a point to make—to Lennon, to Epstein, and to his girl. The storming, leering, menacing rendition that followed made the version that wound up later on their album sound tame in comparison. Jagger didn't sing, he *spat* out the lurid lyrics, running, jumping, stopping, posing—anything to get the audience's attention.

He got it. Lennon's table was still, all eyes glued on this madman on stage. The crowd forgot about Lennon. They'd never seen Jagger like this. They gave him an unprecedented mid-set standing ovation at the end of the song. Jagger wiped the sweat from his forehead and looked around the room. Lennon's party was standing, too. A big smile broke out on Jagger's face. Beat that, you pussies, he thought to himself, as Keith Richard started the chug-a-lug guitar intro to "Little Queenie."

Lennon was fascinated by the Stones, but he was completely enthralled by Jagger's girlfriend. She seemed so . . . so . . . different from the sort of girls who came to rock & roll clubs. Quite different from his wife, Cynthia, as well. He wanted her. He wasn't sure about his future, his music, his money, his talent, or anything else at that point except for one thing: *he wanted this woman.* He figured he could have her, too. Who was going to deny John Lennon anything? And it seemed unlikely that she'd refuse him in favor of the lead singer of this purist R&B

God dropped by unexpectedly at this 1963 photo
session. George Harrison waves hello, others
can't see him.

group. He was good, yes, but surely she could see that the Stones weren't going anywhere near the charts with their raw, undisciplined brand of R&B.

He leaned toward her, and shouted in her ear, above the noise of the Stones:

"You're the most beautiful, most mysterious, most seductive woman I've ever seen in my life. I want to take you with me tonight after the show. How about it?"

She was shocked. He must be kidding, she thought. She pretended she didn't hear him and made him repeat the entire pitch one more time, merely to humiliate him. He repeated it, louder this time. Her face registered surprise, then turned toward the stage and Mick Jagger. Lennon persisted. *"How about it?"* he shouted once again in her ear. She had been waiting, trying to compose the perfect retort to this big-headed braggart.

She finally had it. *"You see that guy up there?"* she said loudly into Lennon's ear. He acknowledged her. She continued. *"He's the real thing. He may never get out of Richmond, and he may never get wealthy, but that's because he's true to himself. He doesn't compromise his music, and he doesn't compromise himself, and that's a lot more than I can say for your group and that soppy pop material you churn out just to make a few pounds. I want something* real. *Don't waste your time on me, John Lennon. . . ."*

Lennon was stunned. He hadn't been rejected even once since he started the Beatles. He'd forgotten the feeling, and now it all came back to him. His mind raced. If only she'd seen us in Hamburg, he thought. We could've blown the Stones off the stage back then. But she's right. She's absolutely right. We have sold out.

He looked at Epstein. He felt a kind of hatred race through his veins. He's the one. He's the one who put us into those silly costumes, those collarless jackets and pointed black boots with the faggy Cuban heels. But I went along with it. I didn't say a word when he told us to bow in unison after our concerts. "It looks professional," he said. *Professional,* my arse. I bet we look like a bunch of saps doing that.

The self-doubt continued for Lennon throughout the remainder of the Stones' set. As they were winding up their last number, Lennon noticed Epstein shaking hands with a wild-looking guy in his mid-to-late twenties. Lennon nudged Brian as if to say, "Come on, wrap it up, let's get out of here." Lennon's dream lady then ran from the table toward the backstage dressing room to be with Jagger. He took a long, last look, then she disappeared behind the partition. Now Epstein was introducing Lennon to this fellow.

"I'd like you to meet Andrew Oldham, John. He's the Stones' manager." Oldham shook John's hand, then proceeded to profess great admiration for Lennon and the Beatles.

"You guys write great songs," he said. "Great songs. I really admire your talent. Really admire you."

The compliment meant nothing. Lennon couldn't impress the only woman he'd ever really wanted. He felt worthless.

Oldham continued, spewing out verbiage at a mile-a-minute pace: "That's been the hardest thing for us, finding the proper material. The boys just want to record these old songs they do in their act and, sure, it works onstage, but it doesn't cut the mustard on a single."

Lennon remembered the one Stones single he'd heard, a rushed-up cover of an obscure Chuck Berry tune, "Come On." It was a failure, both commercially and artistically. Their manager was right—they'd never crack the charts with that sort of thing. Just as Lennon thought. He was about to tell Oldham this, but Oldham hadn't let up on his verbal barrage:

"You Beatles seem to have a knack, an *instinct* for knocking out these commercial tunes that sound so natural on the radio, like they'd been around forever. How do you do it?"

Lennon began a reply, but Oldham couldn't wait:

"Say, you wouldn't happen to have any old material lying around that you could let us have, would you? It'd be a real honor for us to cover a John Lennon-Paul McCartney tune. A real honor."

So that's what he's up to, Lennon thought. Now it makes sense. Epstein, the businessman, saw it coming all along and wanted no part of it.

"We're flattered, Andrew," Epstein said, "but we go back in the studio in a matter of weeks and with the touring and all, there certainly isn't any sort of surplus—"

Lennon cut him off. A thought struck him.

"You've got it, Andrew. I've got a perfect song for the Stones."

Oldham was ecstatic. Epstein was furious. Lennon was calculating. He'd write them a song, all right. Just one. And when they go to the top of the charts with it, she'll know. And when they never follow it up with another hit, she'll really know. And when she sees that the only way her pure, uncompromising boyfriend can make it is through the talents of John Winston Lennon, she'll come across.

"Let me have your card, Andrew," Lennon said. "I'll mail a tune off to you tomorrow."

Oldham thanked Lennon and Epstein profusely, then ran backstage to tell his group the good news.

"Have you taken leave of your senses, John?" Brian asked him as they were leaving the club.

"Come on, Brian. Why hoard it? The Stones deserve a break. Let's be big about it and give them one."

"But what song do we have that we can afford to just hand over? Paul told me this morning that we're still two songs short for the next album."

"We'll give them the song, Brian, that I'm going to write tonight."

Lennon went home and headed straight for his music room. He picked up a guitar and let his mind replay the

DECCA

REGD.
MADE IN ENGLAND · THE DECCA RECORD CO. LTD.

45 RPM

ALL RIGHTS OF THE MANUFACTURER AND OF THE OWNER OF THE RECORDED WORK RESERVED · UNAUTHORISED PUBLIC PERFORMANCE BROADCASTING AND COPYING OF THIS RECORD PROHIBITED

TRUE HIGH FIDELITY

K/T

XDR.31954

RECORDING FIRST
PUBLISHED 1963

F.11764

Northern
Songs Ltd.

S

I WANNA BE YOUR MAN
(Lennon, McCartney)
THE ROLLING STONES
Production : Impact Sound

"I Wanna Be Your Man"—John Lennon wanted this
to be a hit more than anything he ever
wrote for the Beatles.

evening. Rhythm & blues. He worked out a basic R&B chord pattern and thought about the woman. Her eyes. Her mouth. The way she carried herself. The way he wanted her like he never wanted any woman before. Over the guitar he began singing in the R&B style he hadn't used since Hamburg:

"I wanna be your lover, baby, I wanna be your man. I wanna be your lover, baby, I wanna be your man ..."

It was simple R&B—too simple—but he resisted the temptation to expand the song, to sophisticate it. He knew it would have to be tough and basic for the Stones to even consider it, Oldham or no Oldham. And he wanted to see this song at the top of the charts more than anything he'd ever written for the Beatles.

A week later, Lennon received a thank-you note from Jagger. They loved the song and were quite pleased with the way it turned out. Would he care to come by and have a listen? He wanted to, but was afraid he'd run into her. He didn't want to see her again until the Stones cracked the Top Ten with "I Wanna Be Your Man."

Six weeks later, both *Melody Maker* and the *New Musical Express* charted "I Wanna Be Your Man" at number seven.

The Beatles were in the middle of the recording sessions that would produce their far-more-ambitious second album, *Money—That's What I Want*, when the telegram arrived from New York:

CONGRATULATIONS, BOYS. GET READY FOR THE STATES. DETAILS WORKED OUT WITH ED SULLIVAN FOR THREE STRAIGHT WEEKS OF TOP-BILLED AP-PEARANCES (AND A FREE LUNCH). WOULD LIKE TO GET INTO A POKER GAME WITH HIM SOMETIME. KEEP CREATING. BRIAN.

6

Money ... That's What I Want

The Beatles were so excited about Epstein's telegram that they forced it out of their minds. It would have been impossible to consider the prospect of America and still proceed with the difficult task of recording an album. Yet, Lennon caught himself smiling.

"Still think you could have gone this far on your own, Paul?"

Lennon could be so cutting sometimes, McCartney thought to himself. Where does he get off with that bit, anyway? Wasn't he, Paul McCartney, at least equally responsible for their success? As always, McCartney kept such thoughts to himself.

The second album was a breakthrough in British rock. If *We're Gonna Change the Face of Pop Music Forever* could be considered the birth of the Beatles as a recording unit, then *Money—That's What I Want* could certainly be viewed as the Beatles' puberty.[1]

The title song (previously a U.S. hit for Barrett Strong) was a staple of their live act, and remains to this day John Lennon's finest vocal performance. The album firmly established Lennon and Paul McCartney as Britain's premier pop songwriters. Originals like "All My Loving," "It Won't Be Long," "I Wanna Be Your Man," and the

1. But only by those with a penchant for bizarre metaphors.

Money...That's What I Want

THE BEATLES

THEIR SECOND ALBUM—a healthy dose of the honesty they were to become known for.

hilarious "Roll Over Beethoven" (all about the difficulties McCartney had in teaching his dog to do tricks) demonstrated a remarkable versatility that no one else in England had ever achieved.

The sessions also produced what is, arguably, the Beatles' most important song, "I Want to Hold Your Hand." Important not for musical reasons (although it was a fine single) but because it gave the Beatles what they had never dared dream for: a number-one single in America! It hit the top on January 28, 1964.

When the news arrived from America, the Beatles were in Paris, relaxing after a typically frenzied concert. They did two things: First, they threw a party that people in France still talk about. Second, they kicked Ringo Starr out of the group. (This last gesture was done as an elaborate practical joke, and serves to demonstrate the sense of humor that allowed the Beatles to withstand the pressures of stardom which lay ahead.) Ringo, believing he was really out, disappeared for two days, and the other three went into near panic.

"It was your bloody idea, John," Paul said, after they were forced to cancel the next night's show in Paris.

"How was I supposed to know he'd believe it?"

"Come on," George said. "You know how sensitive he is. He still feels bad about replacing Pete Best."

"I don't feel too good about it myself," McCartney said. "You know, Pete stood by us through thick and thin, and we just up and dumped him."

"And it never bothered you that he always landed the tastiest birds after the gigs?" Lennon said.

"Sure it bothered me, but that's no reason to throw him out," McCartney answered.

"That's not why we threw him out, Paul," George interjected. "We threw him out because he couldn't play the drums properly. I mean anybody who can't keep the beat on those simple songs you and John write has no business in the band."

"*Simple songs?*" John was shouting. "Who writes simple songs?"

"Take it easy, John," George said defensively. "All I meant was that *all* pop songs are relatively simple compared to R&B and jazz. You know that."

The argument was over, but Paul hadn't got his two cents in yet.

"I suppose your 'Don't Bother Me' is an example of sophistication in songwriting?" he said sarcastically.

"Come off it, Paul, we've got bigger problems. We're missing a drummer." George was valiantly trying to return to the subject. It worked.

They finally tracked Ringo down a day later in Liverpool, drumming away in Rory Storm's garage. George and John found him in a somewhat-less-than-agreeable mood.

"It was a joke, Ringo," John said.

"Hope you all got a lot of laughs."

"Whatever happened to your sense of humor?" George asked.

"Whatever happened to your sense of bloody decency?" Ringo shot back at him. "You did it to Pete, and now you're doing the same to me. Except I'm not taking it lying down. Rory and I are forming a new group and we're gonna be around long after you three are forgotten."

"You're joining up with Rory?" John was amused. "He get a new wind machine, or what?"

Ringo winced from behind his drum kit.

John continued. "Rory's finished, Ringo. He dropped his load two years ago. You're gonna go back to fish and chips when you've already got steak? We've got the number-one record in bleedin' America, for chrissakes!"

"Maybe you do. What's it to me?"

John was growing impatient. Ringo was still with them. They all knew it.

"*I* don't have the number-one single in America, you

**George Harrison gives head to unexcited
female fan on London's Carnaby Street, 1965.**

nit! *We've* got the number-one single. You've got it, I've got it, George has it, and Paul does, too."

Ringo started playing the drums. He pretended he was alone. George let out a groan, walked over to him and grabbed the sticks out of his hands.

"We want you to come back," George told him.

"I'll only come back if you both get on your hands and knees and beg me to." It was a game now.

"And you can go straight to hell," John said. He turned around and walked out. George was right behind. Ringo followed both of them. He was laughing hysterically.

"You almost did it! You almost got down on your hands and knees," Ringo said. He was laughing so hard that tears came to his eyes.

"Did not," John said.

"Yes you did!"

"Did not."

"Did so."

"Did not."

They got into the limo and drove off.

7

Across the Universe

The Beatles remained silent throughout the flight to America. They were nervous. They felt more like precious cargo than like human beings. On board was an entourage of more than thirty people. Although each had a different function, all were there, in one way or another, to protect the cargo.

They landed at New York's Kennedy Airport at one in the afternoon on February 7, 1964. Although they expected a warm welcome from their U.S. label, Capitol, they were completely unprepared for the thousands of screaming teenagers who had turned out to welcome them.[1]

The plane taxied to a halt. Everyone inside was gripped with a combination of fear and excitement. Lennon stood up, walked to the bathroom, combed his hair, took a deep breath, and emerged with the other Beatles.

They were quickly ushered inside the airport into a large room already set up with microphones for a press conference.

1. Many observers attribute this turnout—in fact, the whole Beatle phenomenon—to the death three months earlier of President John F. Kennedy. This seems a gross overstatement. Historians may argue about Kennedy's performance as president, but certainly he had little impact upon America musically. His two Columbia singles were both flops (and deservedly so) and his guitar playing and singing were shamefully ragged. Still, it must be said that he was vastly superior to his successor in the White House, who was so devoid of talent that no major label even approached him.

The questions from the startled American press corps came fast and furious. The highlight occurred when an enterprising New York DJ named Murray the K forced his way onto the podium to get his photo taken with the Beatles.

"Who's this chap?" George Harrison asked the assembled press contingent.

"I'm Murray the K," said Murray the K. "I'm what's happening, baby!"

"You look more like what happened," John said. "A long time ago."

"I play all your records every day on WMCA. I'm known here as 'The Fifth Beatle.' "

"The Fifth Beatle is dead, Murray," John said.

"Could be him, then," George said. "He looks dead to me."

A voice from the crowd shouted: *"Will somebody get Murray the fuckin' K off the stage?"* Murray remained for another picture or two, then departed.

The questions continued for another twenty minutes, before Epstein jumped onstage to say, "Thank you very much. The boys are quite tired. That'll have to be the last question."

"Who's he?" a reporter asked.

"That's the manager," someone replied. "A year ago he was a plumber. Now he owns twenty-five percent of them."

"Bet he was making better money as a plumber," the reporter said.

On the day before the first of the Sullivan shows, complications arose. George Harrison, who had been fighting off a cold since before the group left for America, finally surrendered and was forced to stay in bed with a 103° temperature. The Beatles had been hanging out with Del Shannon, then a rock star of some renown (best remembered today for 1961's "Runaway"). McCartney

BEATLES ARRIVE IN AMERICA—A nervous John
Lennon spent the entire transatlantic flight
painting a mural of the Beatles on the inside of the
plane's door. This TWA airplane has gone
on to become a valuable collector's item among
rabid Beatlemaniacs.

asked him if he'd like to stand in for Harrison during the rehearsal scheduled that day at Sullivan's studio. Shannon, quite flattered, said he'd be delighted.

The Beatles arrived at 1:30 that afternoon and ran through "All My Loving," "I Want to Hold Your Hand," "Please Please Me," and "She Loves You." John, Paul, and Ringo were amazed by Shannon's lead-guitar playing.

"He's about twice as good as George," Paul said.

John agreed. "Maybe we oughta get him in the group."

"What about George?" Paul protested.

"Aah, him and his God kick," John said disgustedly. "Drives me crazy."

Paul realized what was happening. "You're still bugged about him calling our songs simple."

"What if I am? I got a right to be, don't I? You and me are the talent in this group." He noticed Ringo listening in, and quickly added, "Nothing personal, Ringo, you understand." Ringo didn't look as though he did, but John went ahead anyway. "We have to write the tunes," he said to Paul. "If we let him put even one of those bloody Hare Krishna songs of his on an album, we're gonna be back at The Cavern in six months."

The others agreed there was a problem, but there was nothing they could do about it at this point, so the matter was dropped. Del Shannon, meanwhile, was so charged up about his session with the Beatles that he went right over to a recording studio afterward and put down a version of "From Me to You" that exceeded the Fab Four's original hit in every respect.[2]

Harrison had recovered sufficiently by the next day and joined the Beatles in what was to be their supreme moment in America—their debut on the Sullivan show. It is estimated that one out of every two televisions in the

2. Except chart position. It bombed miserably. A powerful record, though, it can be found on Del's album *I Can Outplay George Harrison* (Big Top 5646).

Ringo and Paul visit with American star Del Shannon in their hotel room. Shannon was a "runaway" success in his brief stint as Beatles lead guitarist.

country was tuned to CBS that night,[3] setting a record that was not to be surpassed until 1977 when "Charlie's Angels" reran the legendary "Undercover in a Topless Nightclub" episode, which garnered a 60 percent Nielsen share.

The Sullivan show was the Beatles' biggest challenge yet, and they met it admirably. There was so much excitement in the studio audience that it was difficult to hear the opening acts on the program that night. Then Sullivan strode to the mike for the magical moment— *"AND NOW FOR YOU, MY LITTLE CHICK-A-DEES!* [4] *ALREADY BELOVED IN THEIR HOMELAND OF ENGLAND, HERE THEY ARE: THE BEATLES!"*

The group got the signal from the director, then burst into an exuberant version of "All My Loving," followed by "I Want to Hold Your Hand," and "From Me to You." The TV screen alternated between shots of the group and an hysterical audience. When they finished the short set, Sullivan reappeared to a chorus of boos. He assured everyone that the Beatles would return in the second half of the show.

Backstage, Del Shannon was chatting with George Harrison. Their conversation was overheard by a CBS makeup lady, Clair Rawls, who recalls it in vivid detail:

"They tell me you're a pretty fair guitar player," Harrison said.

"Well, I get by," answered an embarrassed Shannon.

"I'm working on a new song. Want to tell me what you think of it?"

"Sure," Shannon said. It was a compliment for a Beatle to ask anyone's opinion about anything. "I didn't even know you wrote songs," he said to Harrison. "I thought John and Paul handled that."

3. Most of the other sets were being used for electronic pong games, then the rage in America.
4. Sullivan occasionally referred to young girls as "chick-a-dees." Young girls occasionally referred to Sullivan as "senile."

**Beatles scan audience at Ed Sullivan show
for Brian Epstein, needed for moral support and to
fix a clogged sink in their dressing room.**

"That's what everybody thinks," said Harrison bitterly. "They've built up a conspiracy against me. It's because my songs are better than theirs. They're afraid of what will happen when the public finds out. And they will, mark my words. I'll stay in the background now because the money's good, but one day, you'll see. They all will." Harrison paused to enjoy the prospect of his future triumph. Then he remembered Shannon's presence. "You want to hear my song?"

"Sure, love to."

"OK." He walked over to the director. "How long before I have to go back on?" he asked.

The director checked his watch and looked at a clipboard he was holding. "Twelve minutes," he answered.

Harrison motioned for Shannon to come into his dressing room. The makeup lady followed. He picked up a guitar, quickly tuned it, and began singing a song that Shannon recognized. When he finished, he looked over at Shannon.

"What do you think? A bit more sophisticated than that 'yeah, yeah, yeah' crap, isn't it?"

Shannon had a different opinion, but he didn't know if he should offer it. Harrison persisted. Shannon relented:

"Sounds to me like that song the Chiffons had out last year, 'He's So Fine.' Sounds just like it. Same changes."

Harrison was furious. "Where does someone like *you* come off accusing *me* of plagiarizing? If you weren't so bloody deaf, you'd realize that I just wrote a pop song about the Lord, Jesus Christ. That's never been done before! You think I would break one of the Ten Commandments and *steal* a bloody tune, then dedicate that same song to the Lord?" He was really steaming by now, and only the knock on the dressing room door stood between Harrison's hands and Shannon's throat. Harrison bolted out the door, leaving the makeup lady and Shannon in the room.

The view from backstage at the Ed Sullivan broadcast, where a violent argument between George Harrison and Del Shannon took place only moments after this picture was taken.

"Am I crazy?" Shannon asked her. "That was 'He's So Fine' he was playing. Wasn't it?"

She looked at Shannon and thought for a minute. Finally, she spoke.

"I'm single. What are you doing after the show?"

8

Act Naturally

The Beatles appeared two more weeks on Sullivan. The excitement, far from dissipating with the added exposure, increased beyond what it ever had been in England. They went on to do concerts at Carnegie Hall, then Washington D.C. (where they dedicated "She Loves You" to the memory of President Kennedy [1]). The group then flew to Miami for a much-needed vacation. It was there that they finalized plans for the next logical step in their evolution: a film.

Brian Epstein had been very careful from the start to convey the image of the Beatles as a pop group with *intelligence*. He was properly concerned that their first film be a serious venture. He was violently opposed to turning out a quickie vehicle like the movies Elvis Presley was making at the time. He sifted through dozens of scripts in Miami without finding any that satisfied him. "Every bloody one is frivolous, trivial," friends recall him saying. It seemed hopeless and he was prepared to shelve the whole idea of a movie. Then on the last night of the group's stay in America, Epstein and road manager Mal Evans went to see a local repertory group perform *Kingdom Come, Kingdom Go,* a new play written by Londoner Colin Owen. Epstein was so impressed with the play that immediately upon returning to London, he

1. Nobody understood *why*, though.

sought out Owen, hoping to get the young playwright to work up a screenplay for the Beatles.

Owen was already quite successful and was reluctant to tie his name to that of a pop music group. Epstein persisted. He offered incredible sums of money. Owen said he'd think about it. Epstein called every day. Finally Owen gave in. He'd adapt the play he was currently working on for the Beatles if Epstein would agree to two demands. First, not one word was to be cut from the original screenplay. It would go on the screen exactly as it came from his typewriter. Second, Epstein would have to adjust the leaky sink in Owen's flat. Epstein reluctantly agreed. Owen, an eccentric young man, interestingly enough didn't want the leak stopped. Instead, he wanted it speeded up, so that it dripped twice as fast. He claimed it helped him write faster. Three weeks later, filming began on Owen's work, *A Hard Day's Night.*

It was a bold move for a pop group to make. *A Hard Day's Night* contained no music whatsoever. Owen felt that the inclusion of music would detract from the film's impact. The Beatles were concerned.

"We're not actors, for God's sake," Paul said to Brian. "We're musicians. How are we supposed to do a film with no music? That's all we know."

Brian appreciated Paul's feelings, but he'd already committed a sizable sum to Owen and still believed the Beatles would be best showcased in a serious film. "Nowadays you don't have to know how to act to be in film," he said to Paul. "What about Brigitte Bardot? She's the biggest star in Europe and no one's ever accused her of having any acting ability."

"You're forgetting something, Brian," Paul said.

"What's that?"

"She's got better tits than any of us," Paul replied. "With the possible exception of John."

"Well, then, we'll get a lot of bare-chested close-ups of

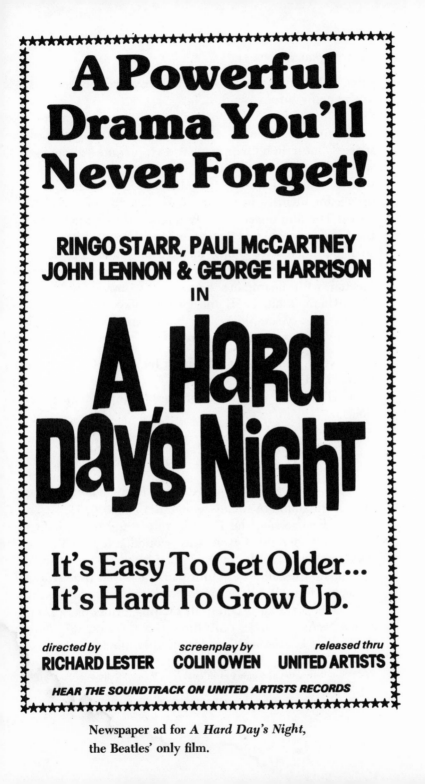

Newspaper ad for *A Hard Day's Night,*
the Beatles' only film.

John. What else can we do, Paul? Everything's signed. We're going through with it."

It would be nice to report that the film was a smash success, but it didn't happen that way. *A Hard Day's Night* was an unqualified disaster.[2] The story concerned itself with a young man's (portrayed by Ringo in the movie) search for identity in the Swinging London of the mid–1960s. The film unaccountably ignored the excitement of the London locale and instead centered most of its action in a public library. Long scenes (sometimes up to ten minutes) of Ringo silently reading book after book were greeted with unanimous boredom by movie audiences everywhere. John, Paul, and George played the roles of menial library employees working their way through college. Dialogue was uninspired:

RINGO: I'm looking for a book by Albert Camus. *The Stranger,* I believe it's called.

JOHN: Have you checked under "C" in the fiction section?

RINGO: Yes, I have. Twice, in fact.

JOHN: Perhaps it's been loaned out. I'll check.

RINGO: Thank you.

The above highlight of *A Hard Day's Night* was as close as the film got to any real action.

Needless to say, the Beatles were stung by their first failure. Playwright Owen was wounded even deeper, claiming that English audiences had grown too boorish to appreciate the subtleties of his work, and that time would vindicate him. We'll never know if such would be the case, since Epstein ordered all existing prints of *A Hard Day's Night* destroyed only three months after the film's debut. The Beatles never made another movie.

---

2. At 88 minutes, the film didn't even qualify as an *actual* disaster. The British film industry requires that movies run at least 90 minutes or longer in order to qualify for "disaster" status. A further disappointment for the Beatles.

TIME
THE WEEKLY NEWSMAGAZINE

AUGUST 6, 1964

Beatles Blow It

It was inevitable, one supposes, that this latest Bundle From Britain, The Beatles, would turn up in a full-length film. After all, haven't they already forced parents out of enough money for their records?

While the news that they wouldn't be singing in *A Hard Day's Night* was cheering, it was felt that such a decision wouldn't have been made unless The Beatles possessed *some* acting ability. After all, why *couldn't* they be actors? If you witnessed them on the Ed Sullivan Show a few months ago, you know they certainly aren't *singers*. Since one supposes they must have some talent to be so handsomely compensated, perhaps it would turn out to be of the thespian variety.

Critical Obligation. Based upon the first three-quarters of *A Hard Day's Night* (I remained in the theatre longer than most, purely out of critical obligation) it is my sad duty to inform young America that The Beatles are perhaps the poorest excuse for actors the silver screen has ever seen.

Not that they're helped any by Colin Owen's muddled, turtle-paced script, it must be said. As nearly as I can tell, it dealt with a college-age London boy's search for identity. Had I stayed until the end, I might have learned whether or not he found said identity, but it is presumed that he would have had to leave the library (where the entire film takes place) to find it, and he showed no inclination to do so.

Of The Beatles, only Ringo Starr demonstrated any acting ability at all. The others appeared to be as confused by the idea of making a film as the audience was in trying to fathom what this travesty of a movie was all about. Avoid at any cost.

—*J. Cox*

A Hard Day's Night gets thumbs-down from *Time* magazine.

Owing to contractual reasons, a sound-track album of *A Hard Day's Night* was released to coincide with the film. The LP, of course, was without music and contained only the highlights of the film's dialogue. For a Beatles album, it sold quite poorly, although many feel it an underrated classic that grows in stature upon repeated listenings.

9

Help!

A failed film career behind them, the Beatles faced more problems. Their contract called for another album only two months after the shooting of A *Hard Day's Night* had been completed. The demands of the film schedule had not permitted John and Paul to write new material and the upcoming two months were blanketed with one-night stands throughout England. There simply had been no time to create even two songs for a single, let alone enough for an entire album. The Beatles were desperate, and had little choice but to solicit the songs of others, then hastily record them during three idle days they had in the middle of the tour. They placed in the major pop newspapers ads which read:

> HELP! We're looking for contemporary pop material for our Spring, 1965 album. Rock and Roll Rhythm & Blues, Standard pop songs, virtually anything except songs about God or Krishna. Forward all material to The Beatles c/o Brian Epstein, NEMS, 1060 Whitechapel Street, Liverpool 1.

The ad was signed by John, Paul, and Ringo. George was conspicuous by his absence.

The NEMS office was flooded with songs within 18 hours after the ad hit. After two weeks, some 15,000 songs had arrived, from both professional writers and amateurs. George Martin had the thankless task of sifting through

Classified

Charge for Box Numbers is 90p. All Classifieds must be pre-paid.

for further details ring
01-261 6122
or write
Penny Morgan,
New Musical Express,
Classified Advertisements,
Kings Reach Tower, Stamford
Street, London, SE1

HELP!

We're looking for contemporary pop song material for our Spring, 1965 album.

Rock and Roll, Rhythm & Blues, Standard pop songs, virtually anything except songs about God or Krishna.

Forward all material to The Beatles c/o Brian Epstein, NEMS, 1060 Whitechapel Street, Liverpool 1.

The now-famous classified ad that led to the Beatles'
Help album. George Harrison was
conspicuous by his absence.

the piles and piles of tunes in search of those of Beatle caliber.

The Beatles were then represented on the charts by a somewhat dated-sounding single—not surprisingly, since the A-side, "Can't Buy Me Love," was recorded (but not released) at the time of the *Money* sessions. A fine hard-rocking tune, it nonetheless sounded from another era when compared to the new folk-rock sound coming from the States, courtesy of the Byrds and Bob Dylan. The B-side, "The Ballad of John and Yoko," was an antique, written by John Lennon even *before* the *Money* sessions. This side created considerable confusion among both avid Beatles' fans and the pop music press. Who—or what—was this "Yoko" referred to in the song? Lennon refused comment, claiming the answer was within the lyrics. These were examined but this only resulted in further confusion:

> Yoko my love,
> Someday you'll see,
> He's not the man for you
> That man is me.

The "Yoko mystery," which began at the Crawdaddy Club years earlier, continued.

In the Beatles' entire catalog, their *Help!* album is unique. With *no* Lennon-McCartney originals, it remains a much-loved and cherished collection, one which is remembered for bringing the Beatles out of the disaster of the post–*Hard Day's Night* period.

The LP combined standards from the first era of rock & roll (Larry Williams' "Bad Boy" and "Dizzy Miss Lizzie," Carl Perkins' "Everybody's Trying to Be My Baby" and "Matchbox," Chuck Berry's "Rock & Roll Music," and Smokey Robinson's "You Really Got a Hold on Me") with covers of chart hits of the day (Petula

Clark's "Downtown," the Knickerbockers' "Lies," and Freddie & the Dreamers' "I'm Telling You Now") and exciting new material fished out by George Martin from the tons of submitted songs. These included "You and Me Against the World" by Paul Williams (later a big U.S. hit for Helen Reddy); "Peace Frog" by American Jim Morrison (who later went on to record the song with his own group, the Doors); "Knockin' Around the Zoo" by James Taylor (who impressed the Beatles so much that he became their first artist signing when they formed their own record company some years later); "Helter Skelter" by an unknown American writer, Charles Manson; and, of course, the song that went on to be one of their all-time biggest singles, H. W. Casey and Rick Finch's "Shake Your Booty." The Beatles' ballad version of this song utilized a string quartet (the first such use by a rock group) and contrasted sharply with the sizzling, up-tempo rendition that Casey and Finch took to the top of the charts in 1976 as members of K.C. & the Sunshine Band.

Epstein encouraged the Beatles to explain to the pop music press the difficulties of composing original material within the framework of their hectic film and touring schedule. They did so in a number of interviews with *Melody Maker* and *New Musical Express* in England, as well as *Hit Parader* and *The Beat* in the States. A flood of articles appeared on the eve of *Help!*'s release ("BELEAGUERED BEATLES BATTLE BATTLE FATIGUE," "FAB FOUR FOREGO SONGWRITING TO TOUR FOR YOU") which ensured the album a sympathetic reception.

Help! remains an enjoyable listen today, with the old-style rockers (especially "Dizzy Miss Lizzie" and "Matchbox") holding up best, and Morrison's "Peace Frog" and Manson's "Helter Skelter" approaching anything Lennon and McCartney had ever come up with for the Beatles. The string-laden "Shake Your Booty," although beloved in its time, today sounds a trifle dated.

With *Help!* pulling them out of the post–*Hard Day's*

The unique Beatles album with *no* original material.
Despite this, one of their best-loved collections.

Night hole, Lennon and McCartney used the next month (prior to the Beatles' first-ever nationwide U.S. tour) to write a batch of songs that were to reestablish the pair as songwriters without peer in popular music. They booked studio time for October of 1965, when they were to return from their tour of thirty-six cities, to record the songs that were to put them back on top.

10

Christ, You Know It Ain't Easy

If the Beatles had lost any audience with the whole *Hard Day's Night* disaster, it wasn't apparent in America. Their first American concert since the film was at New York's Shea Stadium, home of the baseball Mets and the football Titans. Sid Bernstein, promoter of the August 15 show, took a big risk in booking the Beatles into the 55,000-seat stadium, but he knew it. "Ed Sullivan didn't get to the top by playing it safe," friends recall Bernstein saying at the time. When asked what Ed Sullivan had to do with Shea Stadium, Bernstein would mutter something about nobody understanding him and walk away.

But Bernstein's risk was real: he had no way of knowing in February, when he signed the contracts, whether or not the New York Mets were going to be using the stadium that night. (Baseball schedules are not finalized until March.) If it turned out that the Mets were playing in New York that night, Bernstein would have had to schedule the Beatles between innings or at the seventh-inning stretch.

But luck was with Bernstein. The Mets were in Pittsburgh that night and he had the stadium.

This particular show has gone on to become perhaps the most memorable of all Beatle concerts. All 55,000 seats were sold, and the resulting gross of $304,000 set a new record for rock concerts, which lasted for nine years until broken by Black Oak Arkansas, headliners at 1974's Atlanta Mudfest Festival.[1] The concert was filmed and shown as a TV special in the U.S. near the end of the tour.[2] It is today a priceless document, capturing faithfully the torrid excitement of Beatlemania at its peak.

The tour proceeded from one ballpark to another, from city to city. The Beatles began to lose track of where they were. Detroit was the same as Indianapolis, which was the same as Cincinnati, which was the same as ten cities before it. It was always the same. Locked in a hotel room, playing monopoly, smoking an occasional joint, they looked out the window and saw what looked to others like crowds of hundreds of teenage girls. To the Beatles, they looked like what they were: their jailers.

Finally, the pressure began to wear on them. John Lennon casually remarked in an interview that the Beatles had become more popular than Jesus. One hour and two interviews later, he hardly remembered that he ever said it. In fact, even when he turned on the TV a week later and saw local religious groups burning Beatles records because of this statement, he'd forgotten having said it.

Whether he said it or not, enough people believed he did to create enormous problems both inside and outside the group. Adults, suspicious of the Beatles since they first appeared on the Sullivan program, seized upon the quote as evidence to back up what they had felt all along: that

1. Much publicity hoopla was generated by Black Oak Arkansas' management after they broke the Beatles' Shea Stadium record, but a couple of important factors were overlooked. The first was that in 1965, when the Beatles set the record, rock music had not reached those beyond the age of eighteen. It was almost exclusively a teenage medium. Today, the majority of the audience for rock is over eighteen. Secondly, does anybody really believe that Black Oak Arkansas could have drawn that size crowd without the lure of the two support acts, Canned Heat and Hot Tuna?

2. Epstein labored for days attempting to think of a name for the TV special. In desperation, he called Colin Owen, author of *A Hard Day's Night*. Owen asked for a week to think about it, then called Epstein back only four days later. "I've got it," he said. *"The Beatles at Shea Stadium."* Epstein loved it. "You're still a genius, Colin," he told him and hung up.

Unfortunate incident mars historic 1965
Shea Stadium concert as John Lennon is robbed at
gunpoint in mid-song by three Cuban
assailants (foreground) who get away with $200 and
Lennon's solid-gold guitar pick, which he
received for being named *Melody Maker*'s "Guitarist
of the Year" in 1964.

the Beatles were a dangerous, subversive, godless menace to the morals of young America. The record burning spread from the Deep South (where such reaction was expected) to the more sophisticated northern cities. It was a problem felt by everyone with a stake in the Beatles.[3]

Even worse was the situation within the group. George's religious fanaticism had developed to a point where he felt he could no longer be associated with any group that had the sacrilegious audacity to compare itself with the deity. In the middle of the furor, he decided to quit the Beatles. The date was August 31, 1965. The group was in Dallas, Texas, with a week remaining on the tour.

Harrison rode the hotel elevator of the Dallas Fairmont up to Brian Epstein's floor. He walked into the room unannounced, and found a surprised Epstein bent over, making his bed.

Harrison was dismayed to see his manager performing such an undignified task. He told him as much:

"Brian, there are maids in this building to do that job. It's beneath you."

Epstein detested snobbism, especially when it came from someone from a lower-class family, such as Harrison's. But Epstein couldn't play lead guitar, so he held his tongue.

"What can I do for you, George?" Brian said.

"I came up to tell you I'm quitting," Harrison said.

Epstein turned suddenly, stubbing his toe on the base of the bed. "Goddammit!" he exclaimed out of habit.

Harrison shouted: "You see, you're as bad as the rest of them!"

Epstein, holding his injured foot, hopped around the room until the pain stopped, then turned to Harrison.

"What's this all about, George?"

3. Except record collectors. Going up in smoke daily were rare German copies of "She Loves You" on the Swan Records label, increasing the value of those that remained. These 45's go for $50 in today's marketplace, and the gain for collectors was estimated in the tens of thousands of dollars.

"I'm not going to remain in a group whose rhythm guitar player claims he's bigger than Jesus. I want out."

"Hold on a second now." Epstein's toe was throbbing. "John isn't even sure he *said* that in the interview."

"It doesn't matter. I asked him about it last night, and right to my face he said, 'We *are* bigger. What Jesus album ever sold a million copies?' He really thinks we're bigger than the Lord."

"What do you care what he thinks? Let him think whatever he wants, and you can think whatever you want."

"No, I'm sorry. We're a partnership. Musical and financial. My duty to the Lord is clear. I have to resign. I can no longer be associated with the Beatles. All the money and fame in the world isn't worth burning in hell forever. This is good-bye, Brian. I'm going to St. Louis to visit my sister. I'll catch up with you in London. Say good-bye to everyone for me." He walked out the door. Epstein called after him. Harrison disappeared behind the elevator doors.

"Bloody Christians," Epstein muttered to himself. Now they were in a fix.

Harrison was already on a plane to St. Louis by the time the other three Beatles had been rounded up. Ringo and John had spent the afternoon in a high-stakes Monopoly game at boxer Sonny Liston's house, while Paul had donned a false moustache and dark glasses to take Dallas's Kennedy assassination tour.

Epstein explained what happened at a hastily convened meeting in his room. He was visibly shaken, and his voice quavered when he spoke.

"So now what do we do?" asked Paul.

"We'll just have to get him back here," Ringo said.

"He doesn't want to come back, Ringo," Epstein said. "He thinks if he does, he'll spend eternity in hell."

"Shit," Ringo said. "We're leaving Dallas tomorrow."

Brian corrected him: "He means the *real* hell."

Ringo was taken back for a minute.

"You think there *is* a real hell, Brian?"

"I don't know, Ringo, but I do know this isn't the time for questions about a man's place in the universe." Brian was scared and it came out as anger. "What I do know is we've got a show here tomorrow night, and five more scheduled before this tour's over. If we have to cancel six dates, we'll wind up losing a fortune on this trip. And if George really quits, it's downhill for all of us."

Lennon laughed. "Come on, Brian. You can't really believe that. We can always get another guitar player. Maybe even one who isn't a Holy Roller."

Epstein wouldn't hear of it. "I tell you, the machine is only worth the sum of the individual parts."

Lennon turned to Paul, "Once a plumber, always a—"

Paul stopped him. "Cut it out, John. Brian's right. We have to get George back, and we have to do it before word gets out that he's left the group."

At that moment, a familiar face appeared on the room's TV. It was Harrison. He was in the center of a group of reporters in what looked like an airport. Mc-Cartney ran over to the set and turned up the volume.

"So you have permanently left the Beatles, is that correct, Mr. Harrigan?" a reporter asked, sticking the microphone in Harrison's face for his reply.

"It's *Harrison*, and yes, that's right. As of today, I am no longer associated with the Beatles. With the *godless* Beatles, I might add."

"As I understand it, Mr. Harrigan, you claim you are leaving the group because of a statement made by John Lemmon that the Beatles are more popular than Jesus Christ."

"That's *Harrison*, and the statement was made by John *Lennon*," Harrison replied. (Sure is great to be so well-known, he thought to himself.) "I wish the Beatles all the luck in the world and continued success. But I won't be a

George Harrison Quits Beatles

TONIGHT'S PERFORMANCE DOUBTFUL

ST. LOUIS (AP)—Beatle guitarist George Harrison announced today that he has left the world-famous rock and roll quartet, in protest over fellow-Beatle John Lennon's statement that the band is "bigger than Jesus Christ."

Harrison, in St. Louis to visit relatives, said that if he were to remain with The Beatles, it would constitute an endorsement of Lennon's remarks.

"It's the strongest possible protest I can make, and I must make it because I am a Christian first, and a Beatle second," Harrison told reporters at the St. Louis Airport.

In Dallas where The Beatles are scheduled to appear tonight, manager Brian Epstein acknowledged Harrison's departure but refused any further comment, stating that he would address himself to the issue at a press conference planned for 11 AM at the Dallas Fairmont Hotel.

Although unconfirmed at press time, it would appear likely that The Beatles would be forced to cancel tonight's performance in

EX-BEATLE HARRISON—A Christian first, a Beatle second.

Dallas, as well as remaining concerts on their American tour, including San Diego, Los Angeles, San Francisco, Portland, and Seattle.

The Associated Press story which ran in newspapers from coast to coast.

part of it. Now if you gentlemen will excuse me, this has been an exhausting afternoon."

Epstein walked over to the set and turned it off. "So much for keeping the lid on," he said.

Paul turned on Lennon, "This is your fault, John, and you've got to clean it up, or *I* leave, too."

"You aren't going anywhere, Paul. Don't hand me that crap."

Epstein stopped the quarrel before it had a chance to begin. "This is what we're going to do," he said. "I'm going to schedule a press conference tomorrow morning where we will confirm George has left. At this press conference, *you* (he pointed to Lennon) will follow my announcement. You will apologize for the Jesus remark. You will claim that the quote was taken out of context and blown out of proportion. You will say that, yes, you said it but only as part of a larger statement deploring the decline of Christianity to the level where a pop music group could command the attention of youngsters who have forgotten the importance of Christianity. You will then address a personal message to George Harrison. You will tell him you are deeply sorry about the misunder-standing, and that you and Paul and Ringo want him to come back. Do you understand all of this, John?"

"Yes, I understand. But you're dreaming if you think you're gonna get me to do it," Lennon replied. "So what if we lose money on this tour? We're millionaires, all of us. Who cares? I'm not about to get down on my hands and knees in front of the entire world. Why should I? I believe in what I said."

Epstein expected this response. He knew when he got it that there was only one option open to him.

"You'll do it, John, and here's why." He leaned over to Lennon and whispered something in his left ear. Lennon's face registered shock. The others couldn't hear their exchange, but they did hear the words "Crawdaddy Club."

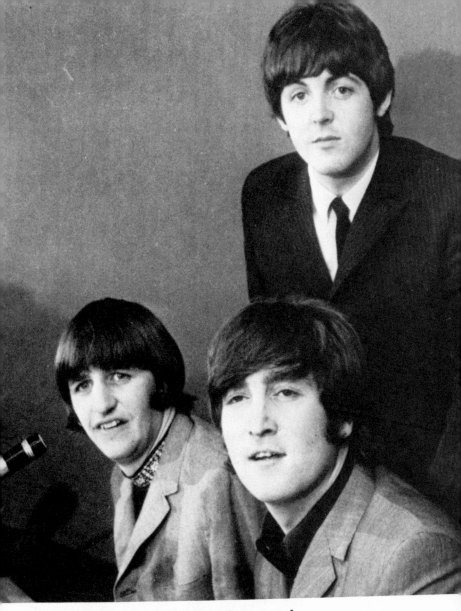

The famous 1965 press conference at the
Dallas Fairmont Hotel. Lennon explained that his
remark about the Beatles being "bigger than
Jesus" was taken out of context. What he really
meant, he said, was that they were *taller*
than Jesus. Since nobody could disprove this, he was
forgiven by both the press and George
Harrison, who had left the group in protest of
Lennon's statement.

Lennon was frantic. "Who else knows?"

"Today, nobody knows but me. Tomorrow—if you don't repeat exactly what I told you to say at that press conference—*everybody* will know."

Lennon was shocked. "You're a son of a bitch, Brian. A real son of a bitch."

"Hardly," he replied. "It's what we call in the plumbing business 'tightening the screws.' Once a plumber . . ."

The following morning, more than seventy-five members of the local, national, and international press were jammed into a small meeting room at the Dallas Fairmont. Hunched around large TV cameras were representatives from all three networks.

Just before introducing Lennon, Epstein whispered to him, "You know what to say, John."

"I'll handle this, Brian," John whispered back. "But *my* way."

Lennon proceeded to explain to the roomful of reporters that his statement about the Beatles being "bigger than Jesus" was misinterpreted.

"What I meant," he said, "was that we are all *taller* than Jesus."

"Oh, Jesus," Epstein said from the front row.

Harrison called Epstein an hour after the press conference. "I'll come back, but I want two of my songs—minimum—on every album from now on," he demanded.

Brian was so relieved that he made the decision without even consulting the group.

"You've got it. Now get back here. We go onstage at half past nine tonight."

11

You Can't Do That

The U.S. tour was the most physically and emotionally draining experience the group had ever undergone, yet both John and Paul cut short a two-week vacation they were enjoying, to refine the new songs written prior to the trip. Both of them stayed up late in the evenings, polishing arrangements, changing lyrics, working out the middle-eights. At last, they could give this new album plenty of time and they were determined to make the most of it. The boundaries of rock were growing, and John and Paul felt—for the first time since they'd attained popularity—a sense of competition. From Dylan, from the Stones, from Brian Wilson. Far from being frightened by the competition, they actually welcomed it. Staying on top was going to be as tough as getting there was, and their motivation was stronger than at any time since the first album.

By the time George and Ringo had returned from vacation, the songs were so clear in John and Paul's minds that they were easily able to translate exactly what they wanted. And the resulting album, *Meat—The Beatles,* went together more quickly than any Beatle album except the first.

The songs on *Meat* exhibited such a high degree of sophistication that most rock historians agree that with this album, the Beatles entered a completely new phase in their development.

The moods ranged from reflective ("Norwegian Wood") to philosophical ("In My Life") to socially conscious ("Nowhere Man") to vindictive ("Run for Your Life") to humorous ("Drive My Car"), among others. George Harrison, with the pressures of the tour removed, played brilliantly and agreed to slightly alter the lyrics of one of his contributions to *Meat*, "If I Needed Someone," so that it appeared slightly more ambiguous than in its original form as a statement of man's helplessness without Christ's presence.

Meat was released just in time for Christmas of 1965, and it was obvious to all who heard it that this is what pop music was going to sound like in 1966. The Beatles had done it again. They had regained absolute dominance over the pop music world.

Meat's significance was not limited to its music, either. A cover shot of the group showed them sitting in butcher smocks with huge portions of meat on their knees, arms, and shoulders. Children's dolls were dismembered and incorporated into the photograph as well. In America, Capitol Records received such negative feedback that within days of *Meat*'s release they pulled the album back and demanded a new cover from the Beatles. The group was willing, they told Epstein, provided the new photo lent itself to the album title.

Epstein deliberated for days to no avail. He couldn't think of anything. Capitol was growing impatient. The British version was being imported by the thousands and was cutting into Capitol's market so much that they threatened to use a stock shot of the Beatles as a cover if Epstein couldn't provide a new one in four days. And if Capitol used a stock shot, Epstein knew the Beatles would revolt.

There was only one thing to do, only one place to go. He'd been avoiding it, but there was no longer any choice.

As he dialed Colin Owen's phone number, he remembered the vow he made to himself last summer: never to use Owen again. Epstein was still angry about Owen

The much-discussed but seldom-seen original cover for *Meat—The Beatles*. Capitol gave in to pressure and substituted a less-offensive photo.

charging £20,000 for creating the title of the Shea Stadium TV special. Epstein had sent him £10,000. He knew while he was dialing that it would cost him the other ten before Owen would even agree to cooperate.

When Owen answered, Epstein explained his dilemma and his need for a speedy bit of conceptual brilliance on Owen's part. The voice on the other end of the phone laughed sardonically.

"Come now, Epstein. You want to employ the use of my brain after you flagrantly insult me with a mere £10,000 for my last conceptual breakthrough on your behalf? Don't waste my time."

"You've got the other ten, Colin. Now help us out. Time is essential."

"This time we agree on the money beforehand, Epstein. I've always resisted the notion that those of your heritage were somewhat, er, underhanded in matters financial, but I'm afraid you do little to destroy such notions."

Epstein was growing impatient. "How much, Colin?"

"Another £20,000 should cover it."

"Fine. Call me as soon as you have something."

The phone rang at eight o'clock that evening. Owen was obviously pleased with himself.

"Never underrate yourself as a businessman, Epstein," Owen said. "You purchased yourself quite a bargain this morning for a mere £20,000. I believe I've outdone myself."

"I'm pleased to hear that, Colin. Would you kindly let me in on it?"

"Very well. Round up the boys, take them to the nearest farm, and have them stand around the biggest brown-faced cow you can find. Then take your picture, Epstein. You see the connection? *Cow. Meat. Beatles.* It's perfect."

"You're an egotistical, overpriced, self-important snob, Colin," Epstein said, "but I have to admit it. You're a genius."

"You will have my check in the mail tomorrow, won't you?"

12

I Don't Believe in Zimmerman

The first few months of 1966 were pleasant ones for the Beatles. *Meat—The Beatles* remained at the top of the charts all over the world, exactly where it had been since its release. Except for a brief tour of Australia, there was little real work to do, and all four were able to resume seminormal lives, for a change.

Ringo, after a brief bout with tonsillitis which forced him out of the Australian tour (Australian Jimmy Nicol filled in for him on drums [1]), went off to Switzerland to study billiards. Harrison went to India and met up with Maharishi Mahesh Yogi, who was later to play a role in the Beatles' career.

Lennon and McCartney remained in London, writing songs, visiting nightclubs, listening to the new crop of records, and taking in an occasional concert or two.

One of those concerts was given by Bob Dylan, the American star who was rapidly taking much of the Beatles' older, more sophisticated audience away from them. Dylan was riding on a wave of popularity brought about by a pair of precedent-shattering albums, *Bringing*

1. After his Beatles experience, Nicol reportedly went off in search of Pete Best. Although I have never heard or seen it, friends tell me the duo recorded an album, *The Beatles Told Us to Beat It*, which was released only in Thailand. The album is said to contain eleven cover versions of Beatle hits, all performed with drums only. Certainly avant-garde for its time.

It All Back Home and *Highway 61 Revisited.* Stringing together rapid-fire streams of imagery over his hard-rocking backup band, Dylan was extending the limits of the pop song far beyond anyone else's previous attempts.

Lennon and McCartney were divided on the issue of Bob Dylan. Lennon figured him for an out-and-out genius and quickly began emulating him in every way he could think of. A not-uncommon sight in those days was Lennon's familiar Beatle haircut covered by one of those peaked caps that Dylan was known for.

McCartney, always the traditionalist, simply couldn't figure out Dylan's success.

"He's writing garbage, John," McCartney said to Lennon in the back of the limo taking them to Dylan's Royal Albert Hall performance. But it was impossible for anyone to attack Dylan in Lennon's presence.

"Garbage? How can you call 'Subterranean Homesick Blues' garbage? We've never written anything like that. We're *incapable* of writing anything like that."

"We're incapable," McCartney said, "because we have talent. And we have standards. You don't think we couldn't sit down and smoke a joint and scribble down the first junk that popped into our heads? That's all he's doing."

"You're wrong, Paul. Those songs are thought out in advance. Every line means something, and on a number of levels, too."

"You can believe it if you want to, but I don't," McCartney said in a tone that meant he didn't want to discuss the matter further.

The Dylan concert that evening was one of those "you had to be there" affairs. Lennon was speechless. "I've been listening to rock & roll all my life," he told McCartney, "but I never knew it could sound like *that.*" Even McCartney was impressed, particularly with Dylan's backup band. "Amazing the way they drifted in and out of the songs," he told reporters from the London *Times* the next day. "One second they would seem to disappear, then the next, they'd come roaring out of nowhere, overpowering Dylan and the entire Albert Hall." But McCartney still had reservations about Dylan the Songwriter.

"They're just words. Don't mean anything," he repeated to John.

But Lennon wasn't listening. An aide of Dylan's had come to the Beatles' box to inform them that Dylan requested their company at his hotel suite. This was exactly what Lennon had hoped for. He was delighted.

One hour later, John and Paul arrived at Dylan's hotel. Dylan's appearance was startling. He looked so *big* onstage, and so little—fragile, almost—when he stood in front of you.

"Come on in," Dylan said. "I'm a big fan of yours. A big fan." Lennon was in heaven. McCartney was flattered, but vaguely skeptical.

"Best bloody show I've ever seen, Bob," Lennon told Dylan. "Can I call you Bob?"

"Can I call you Henry? Of course, call me anything you like. Frank. Pete. Late for supper. Donovan. Anything you like."

This was *cool* as Lennon had never experienced it.

Dylan asked them to sit down, then said: "If it wasn't for you guys, I'd probably still be playing acoustic. It was those songs of yours, those older ones, 'Please Please Me,' and that stuff, that made me consider rock & roll again."

Lennon felt embarrassed. "Please Please Me" seemed so banal, so primitive compared to what Dylan was writing. He wished Dylan had never heard any Beatles songs before their current album.

"We're way past 'Please Please Me' now, Bob. Our new album is kind of where we're at today," he said.

"No, no . . . don't turn your back on your old stuff. It was great. Weird chord changes, tremendous harmony. It turned the whole country upside-down. I love the new one, but those first albums were *unreal.*"

There was an awkward silence in the room. Lennon couldn't accept a compliment about his early material, and McCartney felt slightly out of place.

"Hey," Dylan said, "you guys want a drink or a joint or something?"

Lennon wanted a drink but figured it would be pretty uncool to ask Bob Dylan for one. "Yeah," he said. "Let's smoke a joint."

Dylan produced a perfectly rolled joint from his coat pocket, lit it, took a long hit, and passed it to McCartney. Suffice it to say the marijuana was of a quality that only the John Lennons, Bob Dylans, and Paul McCartneys of the world could get their hands on in those days.

Within minutes, the ice had melted, and it was as if they'd known each other all of their lives. They found they had a lot in common: a love for early rock & roll, an interest in the newest musical equipment, and—especially—fame.

"I don't know if I like it," Dylan confessed.

"Like what?" a stoned McCartney asked.

"You know. Fame. Fame and fortune."

"Beats smoky nightclubs all to hell," Lennon said.

"Yeah, it does," Dylan agreed. "But I feel like I don't, you know, *deserve* it. I feel sort of, ah . . . *guilty* about all of it."

Lennon wouldn't hear of it. "Why should you feel guilty? You deserve it. All of it. You're the best fuckin' songwriter in the world. Your songs are *deep*. They mean something."

"That's just it," Dylan said. "They don't mean anything. I just write 'em. I don't even know what my songs mean, and here I am, people calling me God and everything. . . ."

"Don't let George Harrison hear you say that," McCartney joked.

"Yeah, what's his story, anyway? Was all that stuff for real about his quitting, or what?"

Lennon laughed. "To this day, I don't know."

Dylan continued, "So here I am, sitting in hotel rooms, banging away these words on a typewriter. Words! Phrases! Words and Phrases! Phrases and Words! And one morning I wake up and get a phone call and somebody tells me I'm a millionaire. Beats me." He shrugged his shoulders.

"What *humility*," Lennon thought. "What bloody humility!"

"What *honesty*," McCartney thought. "What an honest guy!"

They were all pretty bombed by this time. Dylan could see that Lennon didn't believe him, so he suggested that the three of them write a song together and he'd show them how it was done.

"Us write with *you?*" Lennon was shocked. Also a little scared. "We can't write like that. We write these little love songs. Little rock & roll love songs. We can't write *Dylan*. Only Dylan can do that."

Dylan laughed, "That's what everyone thinks. C'mon over here."

He sat down behind a typewriter at the end of an eight-foot mahogany table. John and Paul sat at either side of the typewriter.

"Okay, now what's the first thing that comes to your mind?" Dylan asked.

"I don't know. I can't think of anything," Lennon said.

"It's just *words* we're looking for," Dylan said. "Words and phrases. Think of words and phrases."

Lennon was silent. "Words and phrases, right?" he said weakly.

Dylan couldn't wait any longer. "Words and phrases right," he said, then typed it as the first line of the song.

"You're gonna use *that?*" Lennon said.

"I can use *anything*, John. It doesn't matter. Now you think of something, Paul."

McCartney looked down at his cigarette. "Cigarette ash," he said, challenging Dylan.

Dylan seized it gleefully. "That's it. You've got it. Now . . . *'Words and phrases right'* . . . *'Cigarette ash keeps me up all night!'* . . . yeah, that's good." He quickly entered it into the typewriter, then asked John for another thought.

"Where'd you learn to type so fast?" John asked. He didn't want to accept the fact that this was how Dylan wrote.

"How come your mama types so fast?" Dylan said, ignoring Lennon. Then McCartney added, *"At this rate she'll be done by a quarter past."* Paul and Dylan laughed hysterically.

"That's good, Paul," Dylan said. "You've got the idea, but the problem with your line is that it could make sense. 'Types so fast, she'll be done by a quarter past.' Almost makes sense. Now suppose we really get *out there.*" He lit another joint, then continued.

"Now it's 'How come your mama types so fast,' right? Hmm . . . Let's see here . . ." His brow knotted in thought for a few seconds. "Fast. Fast. Fast," he repeated aloud. "Past. Fast. Past. Last. Past. Cast. *Mast!* That's it. That's the one. Try this—'How come your mama types so fast, *Is daddy's flag flyin' at half-mast?'* " He repeated it again and was satisfied. "Yeah, that works. That works fine."

This is exactly what McCartney had expected, exactly what he criticized in Dylan, and yet he was impressed. What a fun way to write songs! Lennon, McCartney felt, was digging it too, but didn't want to say so and prove McCartney correct. As for Dylan, he was *into* it.

"OK, something else now," Dylan said.

"Pneumonia," McCartney pulled out of left field.

"Pneumonia," Dylan repeated. He sat back in his chair and looked straight up at the ceiling, trying to think of a line. "Got it!" He snapped back and started typing, saying as his fingers hit the keys: *"Pneumonia ceilings, pneumonia floors."*

"Great!" McCartney exclaimed. Try this: *"Daddy ain't gonna take it no more."*

"I love it!" Dylan was jumping up and down in his chair as he added this line to the song.

McCartney's lines were forcing Lennon's hand. He wasn't going to be outdone.

"Elephant guns blazing in my ears," Lennon said out of nowhere.

Dylan just looked at him. "Shit. Where'd *that* come from? You got it, John!" He typed the line and before he could finish the six words Lennon said, *"I'm sick and tired of your applesauce tears . . ."*

Dylan didn't stop typing until this line was added, too. "Jesus," he said slowly, "no wonder you guys are rich."

Lennon was into it now. *"Thermometers don't tell time anymore,"* he said, *"Since Aunt Mimi pushed them off the twentieth floor!"*

Dylan typed it all, but not before McCartney countered with *"So say good-bye to skyscrapers . . ."*

Then Dylan finished it: *"You'll read about it in the evening papers!"* He was having a great time.

"I picked my nose and I'm glad I did!" Lennon screamed. Then McCartney added, *"No one knows my nose 'cause I keep it hid!"*

At that moment, the three of them actually fell on the floor, they were laughing so hard.

"Oh, God, it hurts," Dylan said from the floor. "I can't stop."

Lennon and McCartney looked at each other underneath the table. They could write songs with *Bob Dylan.* It felt terrific. Lennon started another line, but Dylan stopped him.

"Wait a minute now." Dylan was wiping the tears from his eyes. "Lemme get that last one. We don't want to lose that last one. Now what was it? I can't even remember." They were so stoned that time was standing still.

McCartney started to tell him: "It was . . . uh . . ." He couldn't think of it. "What the hell was the line, John?"

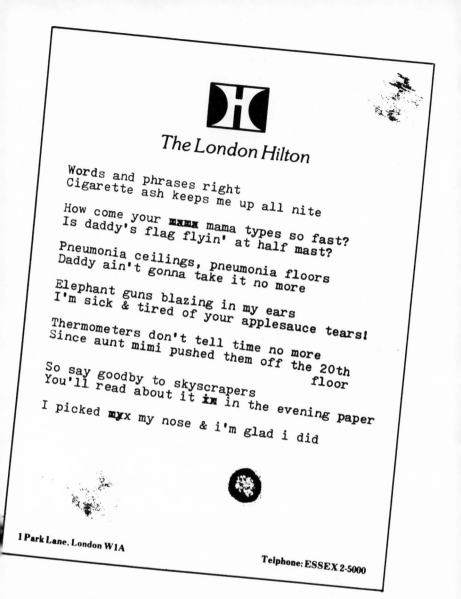

The London Hilton

Words and phrases right
Cigarette ash keeps me up all nite

How come your mama mama types so fast?
Is daddy's flag flyin' at half mast?

Pneumonia ceilings, pneumonia floors
Daddy ain't gonna take it no more

Elephant guns blazing in my ears
I'm sick & tired of your applesauce tears!

Thermometers don't tell time no more
Since aunt mimi pushed them off the 20th
floor

So say goodby to skyscrapers
You'll read about it in in the evening paper

I picked my my nose & i'm glad i did

1 Park Lane, London W1A

Telephone: ESSEX 2-5000

"PNEUMONIA CEILINGS"—Never released, never
recorded, never even finished, here is the
Lennon-McCartney-Dylan collaboration which fans
call "Pneumonia Ceilings." A housekeeper
at the London Hilton fished the original copy out of
Dylan's trash the day after John and Paul
visited Dylan. She sold it for a mere £5 to Beatle
fan. Today it is valued at $75,000!

"I don't remember it, either!" Lennon shrieked.

They all fell on the floor again.

"Greatest fucking line in rock & roll history," Dylan said, still on his back, "and we can't remember what it is! I don't believe it! I don't believe it! . . ."

13

The Inner Light

Compared to the previous few years, 1966 was pretty uneventful for the Beatles, and that's the way they wanted it. The major undertaking was a grueling thirty-four-city American tour in August that the entire band agreed was horrible. The tour itself went smoothly enough, but there was no satisfaction derived from it. Money, yes. But what good is money when you've already got five times as much as you know what to do with? And how can money help you when you're imprisoned in a hotel room in some faceless city in the middle of a hot summer? And the rooms were either so air-conditioned that you could store meat in them, or else they were so poorly cooled that all you could do was lie there and sweat. The only company you could have besides your own was the American press corps, and the only thing they were good for was to ask stupid questions and try to get in snapshots with you so they could tell their friends how close they were to you. And the concerts! Same old songs as last year, but impossible to sing this year. They still want to hear "She Loves You," for chrissakes! By the time they'd finally reached their last stop, San Francisco, they all knew it'd be a long time before they got involved in another one of these tours, and they told Epstein as much. Maybe under different circumstances, maybe a few select concerts here and there, but never again this endless nightmare.

Surprisingly, throughout all the chaos and confusion of the tour, George Harrison was a picture of serenity. Every time it got really intense, Harrison would wander off into a corner, close his eyes, and reappear fifteen minutes later as if he'd just stepped out of a cool stream in the middle of a forest. After a few such occurrences, Ringo asked him about it.

"What're you taking, George? Let me have some of it, mate."

"I'm not *taking* anything," he said to Ringo and the others one day in Cincinnati. "I'm *meditating*. I learned it in India from Maharishi Mahesh Yogi. It's the natural way to serenity and tranquillity."

"Meditate?" John asked. "What—you sit there and *think?* I think all the time. What are you supposed to think about?"

"You don't think about *anything*," George replied, enjoying his superiority in this situation. "The idea is to clear your head completely, and to do this you repeat your *mantra* over and over."

"OK. I give up," Paul said. "What's a mantra?"

George looked at him as if he were a small child. The ignorance of the Western world. Would it always be his cross to bear?

"The mantra, Paul," George finally said, "is your special word that nobody else has that you say over and over again until you have transcended your body and your ego and your petty concerns."

"So what's your *mantra?*" Paul said, pronouncing the word "mantra" as though it were the word magicians use before they reveal the rabbit from under the hat.

George shot him a look that made Paul feel as though he'd asked George about his grandmother's sexual preferences.

"I can't tell you my mantra," George said protectively. "I can't tell *anyone* my mantra. You're never, under any circumstances, supposed to reveal your mantra." George was as serious as any of them had ever seen him. They couldn't stand it.

**THE BEATLE PERFORMANCE THAT
WAS NEVER SEEN**—In the middle of their 1966
tour, Beatles taped the "Lenny Bruce
Variety Hour," an ill-fated NBC Special. Bruce's
untimely death two weeks before the show's
scheduled airing forced its cancellation. The original
video tape has been gathering dust in NBC's
vaults since 1966, despite the constant clamoring of
Beatlemaniacs. Beatles performed three
songs and appeared in a wildly improbable comedy
skit with Bruce which had McCartney
quitting the Beatles to form a new rock group with
his wife!

"Well, excuse me for living," Paul said snottily.

Two days later, the Beatles were stranded in a hotel room in Omaha, Nebraska. It was one in the afternoon, the hotel was surrounded by fans, and there were seven hours to kill before the evening's concert. The Beatles sat facing each other on matching green sofas in the enormous suite.

"Well, what do you lads want to do?" Lennon asked.

"I wanna go back to England," Ringo replied. "I can't stand this anymore."

"I know what you mean," McCartney said, disconsolate. He got up and gazed out the window. "What state are we in, anyway?"

"Confusion," Lennon answered. He got up and switched on the television. A black and white image flickered into focus. "What's this?" he asked the others, indicating the TV program.

" 'I Love Lucy,' " Ringo answered.

"So why'd you marry Maureen?" McCartney deadpanned.

"Probably because she doesn't make bad jokes like that," Ringo retorted.

"Hey, George," McCartney said, jabbing his lead guitarist in the ribs, "check out this show. I've seen it before."

Harrison, who had been silent until now, abruptly got up and shut off the television.

"Hey!" Lennon shouted. "I was watching that!"

"That's why I turned it off," Harrison told him. "Because I can't stand seeing the three of you rot your brains like this every time we go on tour."

"What are we supposed to do?" McCartney asked sarcastically, "sit in the corner like you and meditate?"

"There's nothing wrong with meditation," Harrison said defensively.

"I hear it can make you go blind," Ringo said playfully.

"It's meditation, Ringo," George said sharply. "Not masturbation. There's a big difference."

"Not to me there isn't," Ringo replied.

"Me either," McCartney said.

Harrison, looking for support, asked "How about you, John? Want to try it?"

"Believe me, I have," Lennon told him. "Why do you think I have to wear glasses?"

Ringo and McCartney were convulsed with laughter. John got up and turned "I Love Lucy" back on.

Backstage at the San Diego Sports Arena a few days later, Harrison decided to give it one more try. He suggested they all fly to India after the tour to learn the secrets of meditation.

"It'll change your life," he told them. "It'll bring you things no amount of money can buy."

The other three looked at each other. They were interested but didn't want to give George the satisfaction.

"Oh, yes," Harrison said, "one thing I forgot. It'll get you so high you won't remember your name."

This brought about the desired response.

Various commitments (John did a movie, Ringo flew back to Switzerland to finish his billiards course) intruded on the scheduling of the India trip. It had now been pushed back to January of 1967.

John's film, *How I Won the War,* saw him portray a British soldier in World War II. To prepare for the part, he spent two weeks as a private in the British Army. Of all the impressions the sensitive Lennon brought back from his brief soldiering stint, one stuck out in his mind: the military seemed the supreme example of pettiness and class distinction.

The higher ranks enjoyed special privileges in every facet of army life. Different clothes, different barracks, different food, even different *seasoning* for their food. One afternoon he was discussing the Beatles with his staff sergeant over a lunch in the enlisted men's dining room. It was then he noticed it. While pouring some pepper on his steak, he read a sticker on the pepper jar: *For Sergeants Only—Not To Be Taken From This Room.*

"What's this?" he asked the sergeant.

"That's a jar of pepper. What does it look like?" was the reply.

"No, I mean this label: *'For Sergeants Only.'* Why?"

"Because it's a better pepper. Higher quality. Better ground. You have to be a sergeant or above in order to use it here."

Lennon was amazed, "Pepper? You have special *pepper?*"

"We have special *everything* for the higher ranks. It's what provides motivation in the military. Why push yourself to become a sergeant if you're going to get the same things that you already have as a private?"

Lennon understood the point, but really! Wasn't that carrying it a bit far? Special salt and special pepper! Special seasonings? Lennon had originally planned to remain three more days, but the military mentality had finally gotten to him. He found the nearest phone booth and called for a helicopter.

McCartney went to Lennon's house for dinner the next night, where he was told the entire story of John's ten-day military career, including the pepper story.

"Are you putting me on, John? I mean about the pepper?"

"No. I swear it."

"Perhaps they were putting *you* on, then?"

"I thought of that, so I asked three other people—all from different ranks—and they all told me it was true."

McCartney finished his beer and looked off into space.

"So our bloody taxes go to buy special pepper, do they?" he said. He thought about it for another minute, and something struck him.

"Forget George and Ringo for a minute," he said. "Just you and me. What the two of us paid in taxes last year alone could feed half the starving population of the world.

Sonny Bono understands where that
dazzling John Lennon smile comes from. You will,
too, about ten chapters from now . . .

I'd be glad to pay it then. But our tax money going to pay for special pepper and all the rest of the stupid class privileges that keep our snobbish, ineffective military functioning? Now *that's* ridiculous."

McCartney pondered the weight of his statement as he walked into the kitchen. When he returned moments later, he said, "Now here's a problem even more severe than this military business."

"What's that?"

"We're completely out of beer."

This was George Harrison's moment. After years of trying to get a song through, trying to get his chord change in, trying to get the others—John and Paul, particularly—to do it his way, here they were on their way to India to meet Harrison's personal guru, Maharishi Mahesh Yogi.

That the three of them had come at all was more than he had hoped for. That they would take it seriously was more than he could reasonably ask, so it didn't bother him greatly that the others spent the entire flight ridiculing Transcendental Meditation.

"I'm not going to tell you my mantra, Paul," John said, when he was certain Harrison was within hearing range.

"Well, if you're not gonna let me know your mantra, I'm not gonna tell you mine," Paul said cattily.

John held his hand over his heart and in his best little girl's voice said, "My mantra is sacred. Terrible things will happen to me if I tell you. Why don't you ask Ringo? Maybe he'll tell you his."

Ringo didn't wait to be asked. He dusted off his own little girl's voice and said, "I'll show you mine, Paul, if you show me yours."

George heard it all, but pretended not to. They'll all change their tune soon enough, he figured.

John stood up and bellowed, "Transcen*dental* Meditation—that's when you rise above your teeth." This got a

John Lennon complains that he wouldn't be forced to wear glasses today if it wasn't for the damage done to his eyes by George Harrison constantly butting his head into them during their touring years.

big laugh. Then George said omnisciently, "It's Transcendental *Meditation*—that's when you *think* you rise above your teeth." This got no laugh at all.

The four of them were awaiting the Maharishi in a huge white tent in the midst of acres of rolling greenery. They were all wearing long, multicolored robes, their legs crossed on the damp grass beneath them.

"How long is the holy man gonna keep us waiting? Doesn't he know I'm George Harrison of the Beatles?" said John Lennon.

A young man holding a banana in his right hand entered the tent. It was Donovan, the British folk singer. He recognized Ringo immediately.

"Peace," Donovan said, greeting him.

"No thanks," Ringo replied. "Hate bananas. Got an orange?"

Donovan laughed nervously, then introduced himself to the rest of the group.

"Hello, everybody. I'm Donovan."

"Donovan?" McCartney said. "Aren't you the one with the bananas? You know, 'Mellow Yellow' and all that?"

"That's me," Donovan replied proudly. "I just can't get over it," he told McCartney, "this whole idea of me *inventing* a new kind of high. I thought my music would be the way I'd leave my mark on the world, not *this.*" He held his banana high in the air.

"I've heard your music," Lennon told him. "You should thank God for those bananas."

"We should thank God for *everything*," Harrison said reverently.

At this point, a lanky fellow with sun-bleached blond hair and a scraggly beard entered the tent.

"Are you the Maharishi?" McCartney asked the new arrival.

"Hardly," he answered in a nasal voice that was very familiar. "I'm Mike Love."

Beatlemania spreads to such proportions by
mid-1966 that even Beatle guitars are forced to wear
sunglasses to avoid being recognized in public.

"Of the Beach Boys?" Paul asked.

"Yep."

McCartney was delighted. "They're one of my favorite groups," he told Lennon.

"The Beach Boys are so fat, they could be *all* of your favorite groups," Lennon cracked.

"How come you guys are getting into meditation?" Donovan asked Love. "I thought you were into surfing and cars and all that stuff."

"Not anymore," Love said. "We're into consciousness expansion now."

"In that case," Donovan told him, "try some of this." He handed Love an expensive-looking Indian pipe.

"Grass?" Love asked him.

"Nope," Donovan answered. "Bananas."

"Good stuff?"

"Chiquita," Donovan replied proudly. "Carried it in myself from California."

Love took a long hit, then passed the pipe to Lennon. The six of them were sitting in a circle on the floor of the tent. They smoked in silence for a few minutes.

Lennon spoke first. "I don't feel anything, Don. Are you sure we're doing this right?"

"It's a very subtle sort of high, John. It's not like getting drunk or taking acid. And please—don't call me 'Don.' "

"I don't feel anything either," Mike Love told Lennon. "I think it's all a sham."

This angered Donovan. "It isn't anything like surfing or hot rodding, either. Perhaps that's why it's so alien to you."

"Snotty little bugger, isn't he?" Ringo said to Love.

"Aah, it doesn't bother me," Love replied, pulling his own pipe out of a leather satchel. "When some loud bragger tries to put me down and says his dope is great, I tell him right away, 'Now, whatsamatter, buddy, ain't you heard of my dope? It's number one in the state.' " Love lit his pipe, passed it to Lennon, and said, "So be true to your dope."

"Good advice," Lennon said as he exhaled and passed the pipe to McCartney. "Now *that's* more like it," he told Love.

Donovan stood up. "You're all wrong," he told the others. "Grass isn't the way anymore! Bananas are!"

"You're bananas, Don," Lennon said.

Donovan exploded. *"Don't call me 'Don'!"*

"Hey, come on Donovan," Mike Love said, "calm down. We're all here to find peace, remember?"

"Yeah," Lennon said, "you're supposed to be Mr. Mellow Yellow, aren't you, Don?"

"I just told you, *don't call me 'Don'!"*

Donovan was hysterical. He began moving toward Lennon. Paul and Ringo held him off, then the Maharishi entered and his presence brought a tentative peace to the tent.

The Maharishi looked the same as he did in photographs. Old man, white beard, white robe, sandals, red roses in his hand, and a grin that no one ever saw him without.

"Hello, my lovely children," he said. "I am honored by your presence."

"Were we supposed to bring him a gift?" Ringo whispered, mock-frantically into John's ear.

John whispered back, "I'm sure he'll be quite happy with a donation. Somebody's got to pay to keep that robe clean."

The Maharishi looked at every member of the group individually, then finally spoke again. His voice had a sing-song lilt to it, much like that of very young girls. "So! You've come to learn to meditate, is that correct?"

"Well, we can't very well get a suntan in this getup," Ringo said, "so we might as well." George scowled at him.

"Which ones of you are the Beatles?" the Maharishi asked. "Of course I know *this* one," he said, placing a hand paternally over Harrison's head.

John spoke for the group. "I am, and this is Ringo right next to me, and over there, that's Paul. And this is Mike Love. He's from the Beach Boys. And that's Donovan."

"And where is Donovan from?" the Maharishi asked.

"Dunno," Lennon said. "But you can call him 'Don.' "

"That did it!" Donovan shouted. "That did it! I'm gonna let you have it this time, wise guy!" He started toward Lennon again, but Mike Love stopped him. *"Let me go, goddammit!* Let go of my arm, surfer boy!" He was shouting so loudly that it even brought the Maharishi back down to Earth.

"Donovan, Donovan," he said gently. "Come with me. Follow me. The path you walk if you follow me is the path to inner peace and beauty."

He went with him. As they left, the Maharishi told the others not to go away, that he'd be back shortly.

"Jesus, that Donovan's a nut," Lennon said to Love after they departed. "Thanks for coming to my rescue, Mike. I appreciate it."

"Don't worry, baby," Love told him. "My buddies and me are gettin' real well known. The bad guys know us and they leave us alone. . . ."

That evening, while they were all practicing meditation techniques learned during the day, word arrived from London that Brian Epstein had died. The news came as a surprise, but it wasn't totally unexpected. After all, since the beginning of the year, people had been referring to him as "the late Brian Epstein." Now they knew why.

They all felt the loss. Epstein was a doting father, and his presence afforded them a sense of security. Ringo and John decided to fly back to London. They changed back into normal clothing and caught the first helicopter out of there.

On the flight back to London, both John and Ringo agreed they would miss Epstein.

"No more plumbing jokes, Ringo."

"Yeah. I know."

"The thing about Brian was, whatever he was, he was *real*. A real flesh-and-blood human being, not like that phony guru in India."

"Yeah. I know," Ringo concurred.

"I wouldn't trust that Maharishi any farther than I could throw him."

"How far do you think you could throw him?" Ringo inquired.

"Dunno. What could he weigh? About as much as me and you put together?"

"I'd say that's a pretty reasonable estimate."

"Then I probably couldn't throw him at all," John realized, "but I bet Donovan could throw him across a soccer field and beat the crap out of him, too."

"I wouldn't cry if I read about that," Ringo said. "Wouldn't bother me a bit."

"Me either."

"But what about George?" Ringo asked.

"If he could beat the crap out of the Maharishi," John replied, "you can rest assured he would *crucify* George."

"He'd like that."

"He might at that."

14

Tell Me Why

McCartney returned to London two weeks after Lennon. Harrison stayed behind to continue his meditation training and to take lessons on a strange Indian musical instrument, the sitar.

McCartney claimed meditation was the wave of the future. It helped give direction to his life, he told Lennon. He gave it credit for his disavowal of drugs.

Lennon remained skeptical. McCartney had *always* known where he was going in life. He had more direction than anyone Lennon had ever met. And as for drugs, McCartney hardly ever touched them before he went to India, so where's the change? Paul was the same upper-middle-class, pop-infatuated kid who joined the Beatles in Hamburg. Lennon was sure of it.

"Something has stuck in my mind since before we went to India," he told Lennon one Sunday afternoon in March 1967. "I keep thinking about it." He looked at Lennon to see if he was interested.

"What is it?"

"Remember that story about the military? The special privileges and pettiness and bullshit we pay taxes for?"

Lennon started laughing. "The 'Special Pepper' business, right?"

"Yeah, that's it. I think people should know about that. I think they should know what their taxes go to maintain."

"Since when did you develop such a social conscience?" he asked McCartney. In the eight years they'd known each other, the only interest McCartney had ever shown outside his own ambitions was for the opposite sex.

"Since I saw the accounting of our net worth they did after Brian died. After all the records we've sold, and all the money we've made, we're still not *rich.*"

Lennon looked around at his thirty-two-room Tudor mansion from his back yard. "We're pretty bloody comfortable, though."

"Comfortable, yes. But we've sold something like *fifty million records,* not even mentioning all the loot from personal appearances over the past five years, and all we are is *comfortable.* Think about it—we should be fabulously wealthy by now. And we *would* be, but ninety-five percent of our money is going to the government, and most of that to the military. And for *what?*"

Lennon knew the answer he wanted and gave it to him:

"For 'Sergeant Pepper.' "

"For 'Sergeant Bloody Pepper' is right," McCartney said adamantly.

"So tell me, social savior, how do you propose to enlighten the populace of Great Britain to this shameful state of affairs?"

"Let's do an album about it."

"An *album?* A whole *album* about the British military? I thought you wanted to be rich." Lennon could see that McCartney was serious, and John was beginning to become concerned.

McCartney became animated. "Think about it, John. You're the one who's always complaining that our songs are too silly and meaningless. Here's the chance to change all that. It'd be a *challenge.* We need a good challenge. My dad says that without a challenge a man's life is without purpose."

"Well, maybe your dad can write the songs, then. I don't think I could write fourteen songs about the British military."

"That's just it, John. They don't all have to be about the military. They can be about *any kind* of social injustice in any stratum of our society."

Lennon didn't know what to make of all this. Maybe meditation *had* changed him.

"Who died and left you God?" he asked McCartney.

"Brian died, John, and he would have wanted this."

"Don't go bringing Brian into this. Brian would have told you all about 'injuring the momentum of your career' and all that crap. Don't give me Brian. Please."

"But it's true. I discussed it with Brian before we went to India and he loved it. Told me something Ed Sullivan's wife once told him while he was fixing their plumbing, 'You can't be content to coast in this business. You've got to take a chance once in a while, you've got to trust your gut feeling.' Brian guessed you'd be totally opposed to the idea, but he planned to talk to you about it when we came back from the Maharishi."

"Are you on the level?"

"I swear it."

"Brian was *for* it?"

"Completely."

"Brian thought this lame-brained idea would *sell?*"

"Millions. He said it'd be our biggest by far."

Lennon got up and took a walk abound the spacious grounds of the mansion. When he returned twenty minutes later, McCartney was still sitting in the same spot. Paul looked up at Lennon.

"Well?"

"I don't know. I just don't know." He thought for a minute, then wondered aloud, "Who did Brian go to for advice? Where'd he turn when he needed a detached viewpoint?"

"He'd call Colin Owen every time."

"The twit who wrote the horrible screenplay for our movie?"

"Same guy," McCartney said.

Brian Epstein's last-ever plumbing job was in
Ringo Starr's basement, which flooded after a three-day
rainstorm hit London. The resourceful Ringo
utilized the flood to wash out his socks (above).

"Well, let's call him, then, if that's what Brian would have done."

They reached Owen, explained the idea, and requested his opinion.

"Positively *brilliant*," said the voice on the other end of the phone. "At least ten years ahead of its time. You'll revolutionize music with this. Absolutely *revolutionize* it. You *must* do it. I deal in ideas, and I can tell you, a man only gets one or two ideas of this caliber in his entire creative life. You mustn't let this opportunity pass . . ."

Lennon put down the phone, shaken. Maybe this *was* a brilliant idea. Perhaps *he* was the one who was marching out of step. He gave in.

"OK, Paul. I'm with you."

McCartney drove off toward London a happy man, for a number of reasons. One, of course, was that he had the foresight to speak with Owen the previous day and wire him the £20,000.

15

Sgt. Pepper

Certainly, one could say that Brian Epstein was, until the end, a man blessed with good fortune. It's one thing to take advantage of the opportunity of a lifetime (which Epstein, to his credit, did) but how many of us are lucky enough to ever have such an opportunity placed before us in the first place?

In retrospect, it seems almost as if Epstein had made a deal with the devil. For with all his good fortune, he died only months before the Beatles reached the summit of their artistic career: the *Sgt. Pepper* album. Had his death occurred after the release of this monumental work, at least one could say that he was a man who saw his absolute belief (in the Beatles) justified and confirmed beyond anyone's expectations.

The Beatles spent three solid months in the studio and lavished some $60,000 on *Sgt. Pepper* (an amount unheard of in those days). There was such an obvious level of overachievement on the album that, looking back, you get the inescapable feeling that somehow, perhaps unconsciously, the Beatles *knew* their days as a unit were numbered and decided to reach back into heretofore uncharted depths of themselves to pull out the maximum of what they were capable of giving.

Sgt. Pepper was precedent-shattering on several levels. The social consciousness exhibited in the songs had never before been applied to rock & roll. Bob Dylan had approached it during his folk period, but his nasal whine

SGT. PEPPER

THE BEATLES

SGT. PEPPER—After its release, pop music was never the same.

and unsophisticated music kept the masses away. It took *Sgt. Pepper* and the Beatles to bring it into the lives of ordinary people in England, in America, and throughout the world. It was certainly the galvanizing factor in the social and cultural upheaval that is associated with the late 1960s. It literally exploded the Beatles' audience. Before *Sgt. Pepper*, they were merely the biggest teenage pop group in history. Afterwards, they found acceptance with the open-minded members of every age group, from teenagers to senior citizens.

With this acceptance came a general acceptance for *all* rock & roll. It became a valid art form seemingly overnight. Those who had spurned it as pap being fed to addle-brained kids suddenly embraced it. College courses were soon taught on the *History of Rock & Roll*. And the entire phenomenon can be traced back to this remarkable album.

But *Sgt. Pepper*'s innovations were not limited to the social context. Within the record industry, it was a revelation. Prior to *Sgt. Pepper*, pop albums were simply a collection of twelve to fourteen songs. *Sgt. Pepper* changed all this. It was the first "concept" album, with no breaks in the music from start to finish. One track led into another, and while each was enjoyable on its own, the whole added up to much more than just the sum of its parts.

The album was recorded under top-secret conditions during those early months of 1967. The Beatles and George Martin refused any comment on the work in progress, despite the incessant queries of an endlessly curious pop music press. When *Sgt. Pepper* was finally finished on June 20, McCartney issued the following statement through the Beatles' press office:

Back in 1963 we released an album titled *We're Gonna Change the Face of Pop Music Forever*. There are those who believe we have already done so, and perhaps in some ways we have. With our new album, *Sgt. Pepper*, however, the group and

myself have every confidence that we have completely lived up to this four-year-old claim. You can
hear for yourself on July 1. Wherever records are
sold.

To attempt to describe an album this familiar to
everyone would be like carrying Natalie Cole to Newcas-
tle.[1] But some of the highlights should be mentioned:

The title track is a haunting, terrifying opus, un-
flinchingly dealing with the World War II bombing of
London (a harrowing experience that lives on in the
nightmares of the Beatles and those of their generation
who experienced it firsthand as children). Behind a rock-
solid wall of John Lennon and George Harrison guitars, it
raises the question: What was it all for? For what reason
did we survive? To continue the senseless, pointless class
discrimination that still reigns in Britain?

> It was twenty years ago today
> That bombs fell in London every day.
> Whether we go in or out of style
> I still remember it as a child.
> And what'd we all suffer for?
> For what did we shiver on the floor?
>
> For the "Sgt. Pepper Only" Rank Club, man,
> The "Sgt. Pepper Only" Rank Club, man.

It was a chilling song, one that demanded and got [2] the
social changes it addressed itself to. Someone once said the

1. Which an avid British fan of hers actually tried to do, according to the
January 27, 1978 issue of *Melody Maker.*
2. The public outcry against military "seasoning discrimination" grew so great
during the summer of 1967 that by September *all* military personnel used the
same kind of seasoning. All remaining jars of Sgt. Salt, Pepper, and Steak Sauce
were sent to Parliament, where—to this day—they are only used at special state
dinners for visiting dignitaries. The Beatles were invited to one such dinner late
in 1967. Ringo asked to see what he termed "the famous pepper." He unscrewed

pen was mightier than the sword [3] and he knew what he was talking about. Other highlights:

"With a Little Help from My Friends": This paean to mutual cooperation was attacked in America at the time, as many felt it was an endorsement of socialism by the Beatles. Paul McCartney put such fears to rest in a *Rolling Stone* interview where he said: "Socialism? We made a fortune on *Sgt. Pepper*. The day you see us in Hyde Park handing this money back to the people who gave it to us, then come talk to me about socialism."

"Lucy in the Sky with Diamonds": A lot of people will tell you that John Lennon had Liz Taylor in mind when he wrote this vitriolic attack on a rich jet-setter, who flew from country to country in search of bigger and more ostentatious jewelry to adorn herself with. Lennon denies it, however, claiming only that "it's definitely *not* about Amelia Earhart."

"Getting Better": Considering the social and political situation in 1967, Paul McCartney's insistence that "I have to admit it's getting better" was felt by some to be a reference to his bank balance.

"She's Leaving Holmes": The only lighthearted cut on *Sgt. Pepper* is this tune of McCartney's about the famous Baker Street detective's unhappy experience in love. Typically delightful McCartney lyrics:

> Caught her making love to Watson,
> In the back seat of his Datsun,
> She told me:
> "It's elementary, my dear,
> It's not me that you love,
> It's your career."

the top of the shaker, stuck his prodigious nose inside and immediately began sneezing so much that he had to be taken home, where he stayed in bed, sneezing for three days continuously (setting the world's record for this category. See *Guinness Book of World Records*, "Sneezing," 1975).

3. And much easier to carry in your shirt pocket.

"When I'm 64": In this popular *Sgt. Pepper* track, the shocking treatment that Britain affords its senior citizens comes to light. McCartney sings the penetrating, yet sympathetic, lyrics:

> When I'm 64,
> I'll do whatever I wanna do,
> 'Cause I'll still be rich,
> But what about you?
>
> Will you waste away on some park bench
> Waiting for the muggers to hit you with a wrench
> While I'm eating steaks in Jamaica
> Made more tasty with my Sgt. Pepper shaker?

"Good Morning, Good Morning": John Lennon has said in several interviews [4] that this song is dedicated to those living under conditions such as poverty or warfare or totalitarian regimes, who "*never* have good mornings . . ."

> Sure, it's easy for you to say
> "Good Morning, Good Morning"
> While you pour Sgt. Pepper on
> Your eggs, your eggs
> But what about the people
> In Vietnam, in Vietnam
> Who face each day with
> No legs, with no legs?

"A Day in the Life": Pop artist Andy Warhol inspired the original version of this famous song, which lasted a full 24 hours,[5] before George Martin edited it down to a more commercial 4:24. Encompassing one full day in the life of

---

4. The interviews were actually conducted *by* Lennon in the early days of Apple Records, when the Beatles were looking for a receptionist for their new offices. He interviewed eleven girls one morning, and told this story to every applicant who bade him "good morning."

5. "A Day in the Life" is actually made up of *two* songs, one Lennon's and one McCartney's. Only the selfless compromises made by each Beatle kept the original version from running a full *48* hours!

a blind, dumb, crippled, and deaf boy (preceding *Tommy* by a full two years) it presented the plight of all those who are crippled in such a vivid manner that it made self-pity among those who have their health seem like the senseless and unwarranted emotion that it really is. Lyrically, the song was sparse. The complete lyrics:

> Woke up,
> Fell out of bed
> Tried to get up
> Couldn't
> So stayed on the floor
> All day long.

Repeated over and over again for 4½ minutes, the message is hammered home by a series of innovative devices. It is repeated twenty-two times in English, then once each in French, Spanish, Latin, Norwegian, German, and Canadian. The music rises and falls in a series of crescendos and false climaxes [6] until it abruptly ends with a single piano chord that drones on and on until the automatic record changer lifts the needle from the record. Another innovation of *Sgt. Pepper* was discovered by those with manual turntables: the drone can go on and on for days, weeks, months, and even years if the needle isn't lifted from the record.

There has risen a strange cult of Beatlemaniacs [7] who listen to the drone for years at a time, claiming it increases their concentration, decongests their consciousness, and is easier than holding a steady job. The Drones publish a periodic newsletter [8] in which they compare experiences and share information on the art of droning. According to a recent issue, the world record for droning was set by a Cherry Hill, New Jersey girl, who was called "Drone of

6. Including one recorded secretly on location by Paul McCartney at his girl-friend's apartment.
7. Known as "Drones."
8. *Drone Digest*, 86 Vegetable Street, Kretan Hts., Calif. 95646.

Ark" by her friends, until she lost all her friends. She began listening to the drone on the day of *Sgt. Pepper's* release in the summer of 1967, and continued to do so until the summer of 1976, when she went to New York to see Paul McCartney & Wings. According to the article in *Drone Digest*, she found the sound of the drone to be so superior to that of Wings that she left the concert in the middle of "Admiral Halsey" and returned home to resume her drone listening. She remains there to this day.

16

And Your Bird Can Sing

After the intense experience of the *Sgt. Pepper* sessions, the Beatles agreed to take a few months off to replenish their creative juices, restore themselves, and, in general, fool around in the way that only wealthy people can really do properly. Three Beatles scattered to various ends of the globe—McCartney to his farm in Scotland, Ringo back to Switzerland for postgraduate work on his billiards degree, Harrison back to India for sitar lessons from master Indian musician Ravi Shankar. Lennon stayed in his mansion in England, where, the papers said, he'd moved in a Japanese woman who appeared to be his new love.

But they were wrong. She was not his *new* love. Lennon had been secretly seeing this woman since the time the Rolling Stones' version of "I Wanna Be Your Man" hit the top of the British charts some four years earlier. She was Yoko Ono, Mick Jagger's former girlfriend and, of course, the subject of "The Ballad of John and Yoko."

They began appearing in public together, and it was only a matter of days before Lennon's girlfriend had been identified as Yoko Ono, avant-garde artist, poet, and onetime short-order cook at the House of Pancakes restaurant in New York City during the early 1960s.

The pop-music press immediately realized she was the "Yoko" from a two-year-old Beatles single, and inquired why she'd been kept hidden all these years. After all, Lennon's divorce had been final for quite some time.

Lennon would only say that "love needs privacy to grow" and that by now he felt they'd had enough privacy for their love to grow so strong that even severe public scrutiny couldn't harm it.

It was a lot of bullshit, which Lennon admitted in the book *Lennon Remembers* (Amnesia Press, 1971) a few years later:

> I was scared before *Sgt. Pepper* to let anyone even know about Yoko's existence. I lacked confidence in myself. I was afraid somebody would come along and take her away from me. She'd rejected me once, long ago, and I guess I felt it might happen again. After *Sgt. Pepper,* though, I realized I was a genius and had nothing to fear from any other man. I was glad when it finally came out in the open. All those years of hiding were terrible. Do you know how hard it is to hide a 5'4" Japanese woman in London? But it was worth it. We were talking about it the other night. It was a case of incredible luck. Somebody like Yoko only comes along once in a lifetime. Imagine if she'd come along in *someone else's* lifetime? She could have come along in my grandfather's lifetime, for example, and we might never have met. And even if we did, the age gap might have proved insurmountable . . .

Beginning in late 1967 and continuing for many years, John and Yoko were rarely seen without each other. Their love was deep, real, and life-affirming. As in any relationship, there were problems, and the fishbowl existence they endured magnified these greatly.[1] But John and Yoko found a strength in each other that, in turn, made themselves strong enough to handle it.

---

1. Largely because of the peculiar curvature of the fishbowl.

Milk Bottle In A Blanket Of Snow
(Aerial View)

Yoko Ono's first artistic breakthrough, 1961.

Yoko Ono was a consummate artist who eschewed conventional forms of art in favor of an avant-garde approach that was unique to her. She believed art was not something to be casually viewed from a gallery, but rather that one's life could be *lived* as art, and she instilled this attitude in John Lennon.

Yoko first gained the attention of the artistic community in New York in 1961. Abstract expressionism was the rage in those days, complex color patterns streaked on canvas with little regard for the sensibilities of the audience. Yoko's amazing *Milk Bottle in a Blanket of Snow (Aerial View)* was such a study in simplicity it made everything else on the scene seem affected and pretentious by comparison. Single-handedly, this short-order cook had converted the most prestigious artists' community in America to her way of thinking. Lines of artists formed at the House of Pancakes on 34th Street (where *Milk Bottle* hung) at seven every morning and continued throughout the day. Yoko Ono, from her customary position behind the grill, greeted her artistic brethren and basked in the glory of newfound celebrity. And a celebrity she was! So much of her day was spent autographing pancakes that she surely would have been fired were it not for the fact that she was bringing in so much new business.

Yoko's simple, uncluttered artistic statements soon became the rage of the entire East Coast. Her success gave her the confidence to experiment even further with her style, culminating in what many felt was her most significant work of the period, *Grandfather Clock in New York City That Tells Time in Los Angeles.* It was the supreme example of her genius, ahead of its time in every way. An antique grandfather clock with the hands set three hours behind New York time, it stunned the art world for months. Imagine—the entire history of art, thousands of years—and nobody had ever thought of it! Until Yoko, that is.

By the end of 1962, her work had begun to catch on in

London's artistic circles. She held a one-woman exhibition there early in 1963,[2] where she met and impressed the cream of London's artists.[3] It was also at this exhibition that she first met Mick Jagger. Jagger was astounded by one of Yoko's exhibits, *Stairway to Abuse*. It was the most talked-about of all Yoko's creations at the exhibition. *Stairway to Abuse* was a painting hung so high on the wall that those who wished to see it had to climb up a ladder (which was positioned directly underneath the painting). Upon climbing the ladder, one saw what appeared to be a blank canvas with a magnifying glass attached. Upon closer inspection, the canvas wasn't blank. There was writing on it. The writing was so small, however, that it required the magnifying glass to be read.

One by one, spectators would climb up the ladder, peer through the magnifying glass, mutter words of amazement, look through the magnifying glass again (as though they hadn't believed it the first time), then climb down the ladder slowly and thoughtfully.

Mick Jagger had to see this for himself. He climbed the ladder, tried vainly to make out the small printing, then grabbed the magnifying glass, which made legible the following message:

YOU IDIOT!
You'll do anything anybody tells
you to do, won't you? You'll even
climb up a ladder in an art gallery!
Don't you have anything better to do?

Jagger was so impressed with the anger and the power of *Stairway to Abuse* that he insisted upon meeting the artist. They chatted awhile, and Yoko accepted his invitation to come to the Crawdaddy Club. There, she quickly became so immersed in the blues that she completely abandoned art in favor of it. It wasn't until she

2. The woman has never been identified.
3. Not to mention the artists themselves.

started dating John Lennon eight months later that she began to regain her interest in avant-garde experiments.

John and Yoko married in April 1968. By then, Yoko's belief that art should be *lived* had been completely absorbed by Lennon. It was exciting to him, this thought that his very existence could be an artistic statement. He suggested they record their wedding night and release it as an album. The resulting *Wedding Album* was not a big seller, but was innovative for its cover, which featured a full frontal nude photo of the Lennons, reportedly taken moments after their marriage had been consummated. The sight of John Lennon and his new wife nude on the cover of *Wedding Album* provoked considerable reaction world-wide, needless to say. When viewed today, *Wedding Album* seems charming in its innocence, especially in light of the trend it sparked among married recording duos to decorate *their* album covers with sexually oriented photos. One thinks particularly of the sleazy porn of the Captain & Tennille's *Animal Magnetism* featuring "Muskrat Love" (S&M 56754) and the vain attempt at hipdom that Steve Lawrence and Eydie Gorme made with their ersatz-erotic cover for *Smoking Cigarettes and Staring at the Ceiling* (Private Sock 2202).

Immediately following their honeymoon, John and Yoko flew to Toronto, Canada to protest the Vietnam War. Upon arrival, the Lennons were informed that Canada was not involved in the war. In order to avoid embarrassment, Yoko quickly dreamed up a reason for their presence. They were, she said, going to embark on a "Bed-in for Peace." An artistic statement, it required a neutral country—hence, Canada. From their suite at Toronto's Dorchester Hotel, Lennon explained the terms of the "Bed-in for Peace":

> Until the U.S. ceases its unjustified and inhu-
> mane bombing of North Vietnam, until it releases

all prisoners of war and until it returns every American soldier to his own shores, Yoko and I are going to stay right here in this bed. I want to make it clear that this is no idle threat. We are fully equipped to remain here indefinitely. When we are tired, we can lie down and go to sleep. When we are hungry, we can call room service. When we are sick, we can relax until we feel better with medical aid only a phone call away. When we are amorous, we can quickly clear the room of reporters. When we are bored, we can read books or watch TV. I repeat: the only thing which will drive us out of this bed and back into society is for the United States to agree to our terms . . .

The Lennons remained in their bed for three weeks, until the announcement of the Paris Peace Talks served as evidence of their mission's effectiveness. Those three weeks were chaotic ones for the newlyweds. The days were filled with interviews with virtually every underground and overground newspaper in North America. In addition to the press, an unceasing stream of visitors (including Timothy Leary, Canadian Prime Minister Pierre Elliot Trudeau, poet Allen Ginsberg, and TV's Bob Denver, star of "Gilligan's Island") paraded through the doors of Suite 1221 at the Dorchester.

By the end of each day, the exhausted Lennons found solace only in the hotel room's TV set. The enforced togetherness had frayed their nerves, however, and problems resulted. Mitch Mansfield, a Dorchester Hotel bellboy who spent much of his time eavesdropping on the Lennons ("They gave me a lousy twenty-five cent tip for room service, so I figured the only way I could get even was to sell their story to somebody dumb enough to buy it"), sold me their story. He recalled one night, near the end of the three-week stay, quite vividly:

"Goddammit, Yoko, we've watched that bloody 'Access

to the Arts' Public TV show every night since we've been here. I want to see 'Laugh-In' tonight."

"Rowan & Martin? That's such garbage, John. What does 'Laugh-In' have to offer a sensitive, creative artist like you?"

"That's something that really bugs me about you," Lennon said angrily. "Everything's got to have some kind of deep *meaning* all the time, or else it's worthless. What's wrong with watching a fun show like 'Laugh-In' once in a while?"

"*Once in a while?*" Yoko shrieked. "Once in a while, nothing would be wrong. But you want to watch that same kind of crap every night. If it isn't 'Laugh-In', it's 'I Love Lucy' or 'The Beverly Hillbillies' or 'Gilligan's Is—' "

Lennon stopped her. "Don't you call 'Gilligan's Island' trash!"

Yoko was undaunted. "Just because you met Bob Denver, big deal. Big fat deal."

Lennon was hurt. "You know how I feel about Bob Denver, yet you run him down every chance you get. You expect me to believe you love me and yet you treat me this way? I don't get it."

Yoko wasn't falling for it.

"Bob Denver, my ass," she said. "I knew him when he was a nobody. He used to come into the pancake house back in New York and beg for a free cup of coffee or a silver-dollar pancake. He was so pathetic. I just wish you could have seen him, John."

"Go ahead, Yoko, go right ahead. But I'm gonna put on Channel 2. And we're gonna watch 'Laugh-In.' And if you don't like it, that's just tough shit."

"What I want doesn't matter, right?"

"It matters. Sure it matters. But someone's got to be the *man* around here, and when there's a difference of opinion, all sides can be aired but its the *man* who has final say."

Avant-garde to the extreme, John and Yoko
each spent the entire month of July, 1972 with one
ear covered. When reporters asked the duo
what the point of all this was, their answers were
almost identical:
John: "What?"
Yoko: "What'd you say?"

Yoko let out a long, loud sigh. "Woman is the nigger of the world," she said.

"What?" Lennon asked.

"You heard me. Woman is the nigger of the world."

"What's that supposed to mean?"

"Oh, I think it's pretty obvious what it means. Mick used to say it all the time."

"And that's another bloody thing!" Lennon shouted. "I'm getting sick and tired of this Mick business. 'Mick, Mick, Mick.' Is that all you can say? If you wanted Mick, you could've had Mick. But you're *my* wife, see, and as long as you're my wife I don't want his name mentioned in my presence!"

Yoko was silent for a minute. She was thinking. It had never seemed so true before, and she found herself saying it again: "Woman is the nigger of the world."

"Yoko," John said, "do you really feel that way?"

"Yes I do, John. You make me feel like a slave."

"A *slave?* I make you feel like a slave?"

"Yes."

"I wasn't even aware of it," John said apologetically. "I'm sorry, honey."

"I'd like to discuss it, John."

"Sure, darling. But can we wait until after 'Laugh-In'? I promise we'll talk then."

"Well, I guess that'd be okay."

"*Good!*" Lennon said. "Now get up and put on Channel 2. We've already missed the first five minutes."

17

What Goes On

George Harrison was having a cup of tea with a concerned Paul McCartney at Paul's house early in 1968.

"It's like he's left the group since he's married her," McCartney said. "He shows no interest in anything outside of her and her snooty art. I ring him up and tell him our idea about starting our own record company and he's busy. He's either ordering the U.S. to get out of Vietnam, or he's ordering room service, or else he's in the middle of 'Gilligan's Island' and I have to call back—"

"Well, what did he say about the record company?" Harrison interrupted. Lennon's extracurricular activities didn't trouble him greatly. It would only mean he could now play a bigger part in the Beatles.

"He says to go ahead and do whatever we like," McCartney answered. "But it was the *way* he said it. Like he couldn't care less, like I was asking him what kind of heel he wanted the shoemaker to put on an old pair of his shoes."

"Old Brown Shoe," Harrison said, absentmindedly.

"What was that?"

"Nothing, nothing important," Harrison mumbled. "A song I'm working on. Nothing important." But Harrison was excited. It was beginning to look as if he'd actually get to record all those songs he'd been forced to hide away.

Ringo walked in, holding a pool cue. "Any word from John on the record company?" he asked.

"He says to go ahead, it's okay with him," George answered.

"But he doesn't care, Ringo. I tell you he doesn't care," McCartney added.

"Aw, don't worry about it, Paul," Ringo said reassuringly. "He'll come around. How could he not care about something so important?" He paused for a moment, then changed the subject: "Either of you like to see a trick shot I learned in Switzerland?"

"Ringo!" Paul cried impatiently. "Don't *you* care, either? This is the biggest bloody thing we've ever taken on in our career and we don't have Brian to guide us, remember that."

"I care. I care, Paul. But you two don't care about *me*. I show interest in *your* pastimes, but you can't be bothered with mine. When George wants to go meditate in India with his guru, Ringo comes along. When Paul wants me to re-record the drums on a perfectly acceptable track because he's got an idea for a new middle part, Ringo gets out of bed and comes down to the studio in the middle of the night. But, of course, when Ringo asks his mates to inconvenience themselves *this much* (he raised his right hand in the air, and opened a one-inch gap between his thumb and forefinger), it's 'Ringo, get serious' and 'Not now, Ringo.' Well, I'm not going to put up with it forever. I've got feelings, too—"

Why now, God? McCartney thought. The group's falling apart, and he's got to pick *this* moment for his temper tantrum.

"Okay, Ringo," McCartney said, "You're right. We can talk business in the billiards room, I suppose."

Once inside, McCartney began detailing his plans for the new record company. "The way I see it, the problem with the established companies is they don't know anything about music. They don't care. To them it's just so much 'product' like sausages or something—"

"Piggies," Harrison interrupted.

"What?" McCartney said.

"Nothing, nothing. Go ahead."

"Right. I mean, just the way Brian had so much trouble getting us signed is a good example. That was several years ago, and things still haven't changed. But it'll be different with our company." He paused for effect, and his eyes were gleaming as he continued. "Our company is going to give deserving artists the kind of break we never had. Unlike the established companies, we aren't deaf. We're going to encourage the growth of pop music, and we're going to acknowledge the change that's occurred in music since we put out *Pepper*. While the other labels are signing up all the old-fashioned groups who aren't going anywhere, we'll get the hot, new progressive ones!" He was caught up in the glory of his scheme. "It's so beautiful," he continued. "Everybody benefits."

Harrison was no stranger to McCartney's enthusiastic outpourings. He'd seen them before, and his inclination was to approach cautiously.

"You claim *everyone* benefits, Paul. How do *we* benefit?"

"Georrr-or-orge!" McCartney said, dragging the name through three pitch changes. "I'm surprised at you," he said, and he meant it. "Do you realize how much money our record company's been making off us?" Harrison nodded affirmatively, and McCartney felt like a soccer player about to kick the stuffing out of the ball into an unguarded net.

"Well, all that money's going to come to us, you nit!"

Harrison started laughing. "I'm for it," he said. "What do we call this company of ours, anyway?"

"I've been kicking around names in my head for a few days," McCartney said. "It's got to be simple, easy to remember, but catchy, you know—"

"Why don't you call Colin Owen and ask him for one? Brian used him all the time," George said.

McCartney groaned. "I wouldn't call that crook to tell

him his house was on fire." He pulled a list out of his back pocket and read George and Ringo the names he'd been considering. George liked "Banana" but felt any logo for that name would be in poor taste. When McCartney read "Apple," George stopped him.

"I like it. 'Apple.' Has good connotations. A very positive word. Juicy, tasty, fresh, crunchy, refreshing, healthy. I like it. It has good karma."

McCartney shrugged. "We'll use it anyway."

Now it was up to Ringo. If he approved, they'd have the majority and wouldn't have to wait around for Lennon's opinion. McCartney asked Ringo. Ringo ignored him, and went on shooting pool.

"Ringo," McCartney said, a bit perturbed, "I asked you a question."

No response.

George got up and walked over to him. "Ringo?" he said, in a tone he could have used to ask, "*Are you alive?*"

No response. Ringo went on shooting pool as if he were in the room alone.

George whispered to Paul, "I think we've hurt his feelings."

The room was silent except for the sound of billiard balls knocking into one another.

"Ringo," Paul said. "When are you going to show us that trick shot you learned in Switzerland? You *did* promise, you know."

With this, Ringo straightened up, turned around, flashed them both a million-dollar smile and said, "About bloody time! Now . . . watch this ball right here. I'm going to hit it, it's gonna hit this wall here, bounce off that wall there, come back here, hit these two balls, then these balls are gonna each bounce off those two walls there . . ."

18

Back in the U.S.S.R.

When Lennon rejoined the Beatles, they were two days into the recording of their next album. He and Yoko walked into the Abbey Road studio just as George, Ringo, Paul, and George Martin were listening intently to the playback of a song McCartney had written called "Ob-la-di, Ob-la-da."

"Hello, mates," he said. "Sorry I'm late. Yoko and I were working on a film." Lennon got the distinct impression the other three were somewhat less captivated with Yoko's talents than he was. After the playback had finished, he asked McCartney about the song.

"You wrote it yourself?" Lennon asked.

"Sure. Couldn't very well wait around for you to stop making a jackass of yourself and come back to work."

The remark stung Lennon. Somehow he figured the other three would be as excited about his new life as he was. Clearly, they weren't.

"I've got eight other songs finished too," McCartney continued, "and George has several ready and that should give us enough for the album." Harrison smiled silently from atop the amplifier he was sitting on.

"Well, fine, but what about me?" Lennon inquired anxiously.

"Have you got any tunes ready?" McCartney asked.

"Sure I do. Wrote 'em in Toronto. Nothing *else* to do in bed." Yoko shot him a look that everybody in the studio felt.

"Come on, honey. You know what I meant." The others smirked, turning their heads away so Lennon wouldn't see.

"I've got eight or nine songs myself," Lennon said. "What the hell are we gonna do with all this material?" He thought for a minute and wondered aloud: "Be nice if we could do a double album."

"We *can,* John! We can do anything we like. We're running our own record company now," Harrison said, eager to get all his songs on the album.

"Yeah, right," Lennon realized. "Apple Records. Sorry I took so long to send the contracts back. Got involved in this 'bag' business of Yoko's. Greak lark, that. Climb inside a laundry bag, tie the string over your head, sneak your way onto the back of a laundry truck, and get *delivered* to someone's house. Wild avant-garde art."

"Where's the 'art' in that?" Ringo asked him

"It's uh . . . well . . . you tell him, Yoko."

"Art isn't something you *explain,* Ringo," she said. "It's something you *experience.*"

Ringo's timing was perfect. "Experience *this,*" he said, and holding out his right forefinger, he waited until all eyes were on it, then lifted it slowly until it came to rest inside his left nostril. Lennon laughed harder than anybody.

While Harrison and Ringo were putting down a rhythm track, Lennon and McCartney talked in an adjacent room.

"You've written your songs yourself," Lennon said, "and I've written my songs myself. How do we credit them on the jacket?"

" 'Lennon-McCartney' " Paul said. "For the sake of image, if nothing else. Won't make any difference, moneywise. We share the publishing anyway."

McCartney wondered if he was the only one who cared about the Beatles' "image" anymore. John was under the spell of his wife, running all over the world; George seemed only to care about making sure *his* songs were all included; and Ringo was busy moving equipment around the studio to make room for the billiards table which was to be delivered the next day.

As expected, the first Beatles album on Apple, *Back in the U.S.S.R.*, was a double LP. And, as McCartney feared, it wasn't a group effort. Instead of the active participation shown on previous records, they each served merely as backup musicians on the others' tunes, saving their real involvement for their own material. Even McCartney was guilty of this, if less so than the others.

With the Beatles songwriting team splintered, the difference in Lennon's and McCartney's songs was more apparent than ever. Lennon's tunes were either uncompromisingly tough ("Yer Blues"), deeply personal ("Julia"), or both ("I'm So Tired"). McCartney, unrestrained by Lennon, grew increasingly whimsical and trivial ("Rocky Raccoon," "Honey Pie," "Ob-la-di, Ob-la-da"). Harrison played a bigger role than on any previous Beatle album and contributed several highlights, including "Piggies" and the sublime "While My Guitar Gently Weeps." Ringo took lead vocals on McCartney's "Goodnight," provided rock-steady drumming on everyone's tunes, and hustled every visitor to the studio at the pool table.

McCartney's "Back in the U.S.S.R." was written in Moscow during a vacation he took with Beach Boy Brian Wilson, which accounts for the strong Beach Boys influence that many critics have detected in the song. However, a famous outtake from the Wilson-McCartney songwriting sessions, "Moscow Girls"[1] displayed far more of the Beach Boys style than "U.S.S.R." did. Loosely modeled on Wilson's "California Girls" hit from 1965,

1. "Moscow Girls" has surfaced on several Beatles bootlegs, the best of which is the now-very-rare *Shake Your Bootleg* (which also includes a very early rendition of the George Harrison song which later became "While My Guitar Gently Weeps." Here it was known as "While My Guitar Frets Over Nothing").

"Moscow Girls" paid tribute to the lovely young ladies of Russia's capital city better than anyone had before, and certainly better than they deserved:

> Well, Far East girls are hip
> They really dig to meditate
> And the Nordic girls are so beautiful
> That blonde hair sure is great.
>
> The Chinese girls are groovy
> I really dig those eyes that slant
> And African girls are really super hot
> They do things that the others can't.
>
> But I wish they all could be sexy Moscow girls
> Wish they all could be sexy Moscow girls
> Wish they all could be sexy Moscow girls.
>
> In Moscow they've got sunshine
> Almost twenty days a year
> I dig Dostoevsky on a summer day
> When I'm drinkin' Russian beer.
>
> I been all around this great big world
> And I seen all kinds of girls
> Yeah, but I chose instead
> To get back to the Reds,
> They're just the cutest girls in the world,
>
> I wish they all could be sexy Moscow girls . . .

BACK IN THE U.S.S.R.—A two-record set
that hinted at problems within the group, and
pointed toward its eventual dissolution.

19

Everybody's Got Something to Hide

The Beatles, McCartney especially, were quite aware that *Back in the U.S.S.R* wasn't a true Beatles album. Fortunately, the public didn't notice, and to outside eyes it appeared as though the group would go on forever.

Those working inside the offices of 3 Savile Row, Apple Records headquarters, knew otherwise. There was rampant dissension within the group. It seemed as if none of them could agree on anything, from the type of artists to sign to the kind of people to hire. Lennon wanted to staff the office with old friends from the Liverpool days, feeling they were the only ones he could trust. McCartney accused Lennon of sentimentality and wanted to staff the office with nothing but the finest personnel money could buy. Lennon disagreed and denied McCartney's accusations:

"It *isn't* sentiment, Paul. I say hire people who *we knew* and who *knew us* before all the fame struck. Those are the people we can trust."

"Just because we knew them doesn't necessarily mean we can trust them," McCartney said. "If this is going to be the finest record company in the world, we've got to go after the finest people to work for it."

"And I tell you if we hire outsiders, they'll just *use* us."

"*Use* us? What are you talking about?" McCartney asked.

"I guarantee you—not one of these people will last more than six months before they all run off to write their memoirs on the Beatles. You want a flood of books on the newsstands called *My Life with the Beatles* and *Apple to the Core* and all that crap?"

"Oh, stop being so paranoid, John."

"Fine, then. Have it your way," Lennon said as he walked out the door.[1]

"The problem with John," McCartney told Beatles' aide Neil Aspinall later that afternoon, "is that he's first, last, and always an *artist*. Which is fine, but we've got a business to run here." [2]

McCartney's awareness of the necessities of business caused him to abandon early in the company's history his idealistic dream for Apple as a haven for struggling talent deserving a break. Those present at Apple during the first chaotic months remember all too well the confusion created by the hundreds of aspiring musicians who showed up every morning for a crack at the big time. Nat T. Dreser, an interior decorator who was working on the Apple offices in its early days recalls the daily madhouse in his book *Polishing the Apple—Confessions of the Beatles' Interior Decorator* (Steyn and Dai, 1972):

> . . . It was like a *zoo* in there, I swear it. Every day these animals, these *vermin*, would congregate in the corridors and the halls, asking for one of the boys, demanding that someone listen to their pathetic songs. Of course, no one *ever* obliged. And I don't blame them one little bit! With their tattered clothes, their *abysmal* manners, their *tacky* girlfriends in *filthy* levis, it made you want to call a big, muscular maintenance man in to hose them all

1. From *Peeling the Apple—The View from the Reception Desk* by Apple receptionist Lynn Sane (Random House, 1971).
2. From *Apple Source—What the Beatles Are Really Like* by Apple gardener Maurice Less (Bench Press, 1970).

down. My goodness, it was *quite* impossible to work
in that environment.

Although no new talent was being signed off the street,
Apple *was* on the lookout for artists to join the label.
McCartney's friend Peter Asher (once a member of the
popular English duo Chad and Jeremy, later a successful
producer for Peter and Gordon, Linda Ronstadt, and
others) brought James Taylor to the label. Taylor proved
to be quite a find [3] as did Welsh singer Mary Hopkin,
whose "Those Were the Days" was Apple's first non-
Beatle hit single, ultimately selling over two million copies
worldwide.[4] An American studio musician used by the
Beatles, Billy Preston, was looking for a way aboard the
label and found it when he wrote a song, "That's the Way
God Planned It." George Harrison signed him on the basis
of the title alone.[5]

With all this talent, however, the only consistent
sellers on the Apple label were the Beatles themselves. But
as fast as they brought money to the company, it was
being spent faster to support the other, nonselling, artists.
To their horror, the Beatles were going broke.[6] For all
McCartney's brave talk about signing the most progressive
groups, Apple finally put their biggest push behind a band
of Beatle sound-alikes, Badfinger.

Badfinger enjoyed some brief success, based mainly on
the novelty of their early-Beatle sound. It was short-lived,
however, and Apple soon found itself in deep financial
trouble. Lennon panicked, and called a meeting with the
others to discuss the problem.

---

3. For his next label, Warner Brothers. His Apple album was a dud.
4. Hopkin disappeared into obscurity soon thereafter, not to be heard from again
for several years, until the publication of her book *Those Were the Days—
Remembrances of Apple and the Beatles* (Ransom House, 1972).
5. From *Apple (in) Cider—An Insider's Story* by Apple coffee-girl Candy Coating
(Dutton, Pay & Cheets, 1971).
6. From *An Inside Account of Apple* by Apple accountant Stan Tolose (Double
Books, 1973).

"I don't want to end up like Mickey Rooney," he told them.

"Then stop getting married so much," Ringo said.

"Come on, Ringo. You know what I mean. He made millions and then had to file for bankruptcy. That ain't gonna happen to me."

"I've got the solution," McCartney said. "None of us have anything to worry about." He paused to let the anticipation build, then continued: "It's my girlfriend, Linda."

"Stop playing games, Paul," Harrison said. "She sings worse than Yoko."

"No, no, no. I don't want to sign *her* up. It's her father. He's a financial wizard. Perhaps you've heard of him. Lee Eastman?"

None of them had ever heard of Lee Eastman.

"Eastman-*Kodak?*" McCartney added.

"The photo company!" Lennon said.

"Right!"

"Good. Then he can take pictures of us standing in the unemployment line."

"And you have a better plan, John?"

"It just so happens I do. I'd like you all to consider the plight of the Rolling Stones. Do you suppose *they're* spending this lovely Sunday afternoon worrying about impending financial ruin? Not very likely. And I should remind you they've made only *one-fifth* the money we've made worldwide. The difference, you ask? One man: Allen Klein, their manager. He knows how to make money with money."

McCartney wouldn't hear of it. He wanted his future father-in-law.

"Klein? You want *him* to manage us? I've read enough stories about him already. I sure don't want to read any with *our* names in them. And I'll be damned if I let the Beatles be managed by the same guy who handles Herman's Hermits and the Dave Clark Five. We've got a reputation to consider!"

"What's the matter with Herman's Hermits?" Ringo interjected. He started humming "I'm Henry the Eighth." Financial matters bored the daylights out of him. He wanted to be home with his billiard table.

"Well, I'm for Klein," Lennon said. "Mick's always raving about him—"

"And Yoko's always raving about Mick," Paul cut in, hitting Lennon in a vulnerable spot.

"Next time you say that, I'll bash your bloody head in!"

George played peacemaker. "Back off, you two. We're going broke, remember? I say we should go with Klein. At least we can look to the Stones. He's done well for them. What do we know about this Eastman? Can you show me *his* success in pop music? Or even in plumbing for that matter?"

McCartney was worried. He hadn't planned on this.

"How about you, Ringo?" John asked, looking for a majority.

Paul jumped in. "Think about it first, Ringo. The Beatles managed by the same guy who handled the Dave Clark Five? It's going to hurt us."

Ringo considered this. "I can't say I like it," he told John.

But John understood Ringo's motivations and how to manipulate them far better than Paul did.

"Look at it this way—you vote with Paul and we'll be here all day arguing. You vote with us, and you're home playing pool inside of thirty minutes."

Ringo pointed his finger at John. "I *can* say I like that," he said through a smile. "Its Klein for me. That's three to one. Settled. Let's go home."

"Not so fast," McCartney said. He wasn't about to lose this battle. "Klein can manage the three of you, but he isn't managing me."

"We took a vote," Lennon said. "Fair and square. You lost."

"I know," McCartney admitted. "But this time I can't go along with the majority. This is something I feel too strongly about."

"*Paul,*" Lennon pleaded, "if you don't change your mind, you're going to break up the Beatles."

"And you're the one who's always trying to hold us together," Harrison added. "I don't believe I'm hearing this."

"*I'm* not breaking us up!" McCartney bellowed, defending himself. "It's you three with your thick skulls who are breaking us up!"

"No it isn't Paul," Harrison corrected. "It's you and you alone. *You are breaking up the Beatles.* Today. Right now. In this room." It was shock treatment. Harrison figured it was his last chance.

"I'm sorry, George," McCartney said. "I won't take the blame for this. It's not *my* fault the three of you are so dim you can't even see what's good for you."

"Well, *I'm* certainly not about to take the blame," Lennon said defiantly.

Ringo rose to his feet. "Wait a minute! Shut up John! Shut up George! Shut up Paul!" He'd gotten their attention. "*I'll* take the blame. Does everyone feel better now?"

He walked out of the building.[7]

---

7. Entire Beatles' breakup conversation from *Apple Bites the Dust—The Beatles' Last Days* by Apple custodian Dusty Flores (Fullcourt Press, 1972).

20

You Won't See Me

One week later at a press conference called by Allen Klein in London, the announcement was made: the Beatles had dissolved their partnership and Allen Klein was managing the individual careers of John Lennon, George Harrison, and Ringo Starr. When reached by a stunned press, McCartney confirmed Klein's statement, but refused any further comment, claiming that everything he had to say would be on his first solo album, currently in the works.

Nobody, especially the Beatles themselves, expected the magnitude of the shock waves that reverberated worldwide within hours of the announcement. To their fans—to everyone, in fact—they were the '60s. Their demise in the middle of 1969 brought the '60s to an abrupt ending that was traumatic in its suddenness.

Historians could only recall two previous instances when the world had mourned a loss this deeply. First was the assassination of President John F. Kennedy, and, second, when Martin Landau and Barbara Bain left "Mission Impossible."

In *Rolling Stone*'s issue devoted to the breakup a number of cultural heroes gave their impressions of the announcement.

• Mick Jagger (still privately smarting from the loss to Lennon of Yoko Ono) said: "I always knew they wouldn't last. I used to tell Brian Jones they were just a flash in the pan . . ."

• Donovan (in 1969 still an important cultural voice)

said: "It made me want to cry. We were all so close. They called me 'Don.' In a way, the Beatles were like beautiful flowers in a beautiful garden. Flowers have their day in the sun, they make the world better for it, but they have to die someday. What? They *didn't* die? So what's the big deal? ..."

• Prophet of psychedelic drugs Timothy Leary: "I met John Lennon last year in Toronto. Unfortunately, I don't remember him at all. I *do* remember his wife, though. What does he see in her, anyway?"

• Elton John: "I'm flattered that you asked me, since my first American album isn't even coming out until next year. But I'm going to be big, and I thank the Beatles for getting the hell out of my way ..."

• Peter, Paul, and Mary: "I dig the Mamas and the Papas ..." (Peter). "And the hip Sunset Strip in L.A. ..." (Paul). "They had a good thing going when the words didn't get in the way ..." (Mary).

• Dave Clark (of the Dave Clark Five): "I'm sorry to see them go. I think the keen sense of competition we've always had between our group and theirs has been beneficial for both of us ..."

• Billy Preston: "The breakup of the Beatles means many things. It means no longer will we have them to point out the musical future for us. It means no more *Sgt. Pepper's*. It means no more of the joy we got from John Lennon and Paul McCartney blending their beautiful voices together. And it also means I'm probably going to have to start hunting for another label."

Rolling Stone tried valiantly to include what it felt would be the most important voice of all in the special "breakup" edition, Bob Dylan. But Dylan refused comment. The magazine persisted, and Dylan finally gave in. He left a brief, but typically incisive message on a shopping list in the garbage can behind his house in Woodstock. Fished out by Dylanologist J. J. Weberman and hand-delivered to *Rolling Stone*, it was published in the following issue and proved to be worth the wait. As always, Dylan was miles ahead of everyone else in his insight:

"The Beatles have broken up. It can only mean they will no longer be making records together."

While Dylan's statement was accurate, there remained the problem of the album the Beatles had been working on prior to the breakup.

There were twelve songs in the works, all of them in various stages of completion, and none of them fully produced or instrumentally augmented enough to warrant release. With Lennon and McCartney not on speaking terms, the tapes gathered dust in the Abbey Road studio during the months following the breakup. But the Beatles owed Capitol, the U.S. distributor for Apple, one more album before the end of the year. Lennon wired McCartney at his home in Scotland where the latter was working on his first solo album:

SINCE NO SOLUTION AS REGARDS THE TAPES APPEARS TO BE FORTHCOMING FROM YOU, I HAVE RETAINED THE SERVICES OF PHIL SPECTOR TO PRODUCE THE TAPES INTO AN ALBUM. GEORGE, RINGO, AND MYSELF FEEL IT IS IMPORTANT TO UTILIZE A PRODUCER OF SPECTOR'S STATURE, AS THIS WILL BE THE FINAL BEATLE LP, AND WILL HAVE, I SUPPOSE, A CERTAIN AMOUNT OF HISTORICAL SIGNIFICANCE. I SUPPOSE ALSO THAT YOU WILL DISAGREE WITH OUR CHOICE OF PRODUCER IF FOR NO OTHER REASON THAN TO CONTINUE YOUR TREND. IF YOU HAVE ANOTHER SUGGESTION AS TO PRODUCER, PLEASE MAKE IT KNOWN TO ME IMMEDIATELY. (PLEASE DO NOT ASK TO USE LEE EASTMAN!)

—AS ALWAYS,

JL

After a week, McCartney still hadn't responded, so Lennon handed the tapes over to Spector, the American

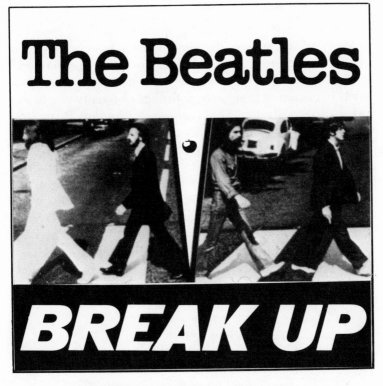

The Beatles

BREAK UP

THEIR FINAL ALBUM—Making sure
everyone got the message.

producer best known for his famous "Wall of Sound." [1]
Many accuse Spector of being somewhat heavy-handed in
his production of the resulting album, *The Beatles Break
Up*. Those of this opinion feel his insistence upon using
every citizen of London over the age of twenty-one to sing
backup vocals to "The Long and Winding Road," for
example, was both foolhardy and expensive.

But whatever controversy Spector created, he *did*
transform the raw tapes into an album. *The Beatles Break
Up* (John called Colin Owen who came up with the album
title in only one week, and for a mere £30,000) was a
continuation of the trend started with *Back in the U.S.S.R.*
Each Beatle grudgingly worked on the other's songs,
saving his inspiration and energy for his own material.

The songs which have held up best include Lennon's
"Instant Karma," an ode to the joys of the popular English
breakfast drink:

> Instant Karma
> Mix it with milk
> Goes down your throat
> Smooth as silk.
>
> Makes you big
> Makes you strong
> Makes you a genius
> Makes you belong.

Harrison's beautiful "Something" was the album's
biggest hit single and marked George's maturation as a
songwriter fully the equal of the more-celebrated Lennon
and McCartney:

---

1. The "Wall of Sound" was Spector's invention. It surrounded his Beverly Hills
estate and afforded him the complete privacy he craved. Anyone attempting to
climb over or break through it set off an alarm that blasted out the Ronettes
singing "Be My Baby" at such massive decibels that the intruders were rendered
instantaneously deaf.

Something in the way she moves
Makes me wonder about myself
Everytime I find out her new address
She moves to somewhere else.

I'd like to try to ask her
If this means she doesn't care
But there's something in the way she moves
And she's just moved away somewhere.

Several critics felt that McCartney's "The Long and Winding Road" was actually a cleverly disguised message to the other Beatles. Mainly that McCartney had had enough and was ready to leave the group. The song is so ambiguous, however, it's difficult to be sure:

I'm ready to leave the group
And head down that long and winding road
To record a solo album in Scotland
At my home knee-deep in snow.

Some will say I'm a quitter
They'll say that I'm not tough
But to them I say the following:
I have had enough.

So, with *The Beatles Break Up* an important chapter of popular musical history had come to a conclusion. Still, one question remained. It was a question that *Village Voice* reporter Cy Mahack asked Bob Dylan a year later in an exclusive interview: *"Did the Beatles end the sixties or did the sixties end the Beatles?"* Dylan's answer, as always, said it for all of us:

"I don't know."

21

Think for Yourself

The prevailing public attitude at the time went something like this: Yes, we have to accept it, the Beatles have broken up. But it could have ended worse for them. Ask Buddy Holly. Ask the Big Bopper. Ask Brian Jones. For that matter, ask Brian Epstein. And if they no longer have each other, they'll still have their talent. Many people, in fact, were under the impression that since the Beatles were so great together, they'd be four times as great apart.[1]

One problem they faced was inevitable: As former Beatles, expectations for their albums were so high that disappointment was inevitable no matter how good their solo work. Another problem was that their solo work was usually terrible.

McCartney's *McCartney* [2] hit the marketplace first. It was released only days after *The Beatles Break Up*, putting Paul in the unfortunate position of having to compete with himself. The reviews were, without exception, terrible. It was as if every publication assigned *McCartney* to their poorest writers. *Rolling Stone's* review was replete with dangling participles, misplaced modifiers, and cha-

1. Unfortunately, these same people were also under the impression that an ozone layer was somebody who made love to ozones.
2. *Not* (although you might suspect it), suggested by Colin Owen. Owen's suggestion for the title, he told *Melody Maker,* was *Paul McCartney.* "*McCartney* simply doesn't say enough," he claimed, and added, "that's also an accurate review of the album."

otic sentence structure. The review from *New Musical Express* was no better. Eight misspellings, faulty grammar, incorrect use of apostrophe, and several spastic colons.

But as bad as the reviews were, the album was worse. McCartney, now totally free of Lennon's influence, filled his debut solo effort with the most trivial songs ever to appear on a rock record. For sheer pointlessness only two other albums in rock history ever approached it: *Ram*, McCartney's second solo album, and *Red Rose Speedway*, his third.

For George Harrison, the Beatles' breakup meant he'd finally be able to get on an album all the songs he'd been writing during the past years. It was the biggest mistake he ever made, perhaps the supreme example of the problems created by overconfidence. The album, *All Things Must Pass*,[3] was a three-record repository for eight years' worth of Harrison compositions. As such, it used up everything he had and left nothing for his subsequent solo albums. The situation deteriorated to the point that by 1977 Harrison was so desperate for material he was reduced to recording songs about his own legal problems ("This Song"), and even about doorbells ("Ding Dong")! It was shocking, especially in light of the critical vinyl shortage occurring at the time.

Surprisingly enough, of all the solo Beatles, Ringo Starr fared best. He found a producer who provided him with exceptionally commercial songs and, through studio magic, a voice to sing them with. In 1971, he enjoyed one hit single after another. First was Three Dog Night's "Family of Man," then Lobo's "Me and You and a Dog Named Boo," followed by his favorite song of the year, James Taylor's "Fire and Rain." Ringo had a big hit

---

3. The title came from Colin Owen's *doctor*, of all people, who was summoned to a Mexican restaurant by Owen when the food he and Harrison had been eating had given them both severe stomach pains.

himself that year with "Photograph." After "Photograph," he enjoyed more hit singles: Creedence Clearwater's "Sweet Hitchhiker," Tommy James's "Draggin' the Line," Paul Revere and the Raiders' "Indian Reservation," the Stones' "Brown Sugar," and, finally, had another hit of his own, "You're Sixteen." He enjoyed still more hits afterwards, but space is limited.

As with every other facet of his career, John Lennon's solo years were always interesting, unpredictable, and amusing. After the breakup he immediately—to the amazement of the entire music world—established a deep friendship with Sonny Bono and his wife, Cher.

"What could John Lennon possibly have in common with Sonny Bono?" was the prevailing question in September 1971, when *Rolling Stone* broke the story. Many things, it turned out. Both had wives with long, dark hair, both had silver Rolls-Royces, and both used Ipana toothpaste (a brand that had been off the market for several years). Bono had a huge stockpile of Ipana and many felt this was the basis of Lennon's initial attraction. They were mistaken.

John and Yoko were, at the time, undergoing treatment with psychologist Dr. Arthur Janov, creator of "Primal Scream" therapy. This school of thought subscribed to the belief that we all walk around with too much pent-up emotional baggage, too much rage. Keeping it inside only caused pain, Janov felt. The answer was in *screaming*—as loudly and as often as possible. After a primal scream, a person could find, they said, a sort of serenity not possible outside of meditation, yoga, or Valium.

There were problems for Lennon in the early stages, however.

"It's difficult for me to scream, Arthur," Lennon told the doctor on his second visit.

"Difficult? Why?"

RANDOM NOTES

Rock Makes Strange Bedfellows Dept. (A Continuing Series)—Following up on a tip that **Yoko Ono** was recently seen with **Cher** (yes, of **Sonny &** fame) we contacted **John Lennon** at his Benedict Canyon estate, hoping to get a bit more light shed on this incredible story. Turns out that John and **Sonny** have become inseparable in recent weeks. A possible clue to the attraction: Sonny Bono has what insiders describe as the world's largest cache of Ipana Toothpaste, the well-known brand marketed in the 1950s and 60s, but no longer being manufactured. During the past few years, superstar enamel has become so enamored of the fabled toothpaste, that status-conscious socialites have been known to pay as much as $75 per tube! Remember, you read it here first...

Rolling Stone scooped the world when they broke the Lennon-Bono story in the "Random Notes" section of the September 26, 1971 issue.

"I don't know. I guess it's hard for me to get worked up enough. I mean, I've conquered the world already. My every desire is catered to by a loving wife and a staff of twenty. What the hell am I going to get upset about? That they're taking two million dollars from me in taxes this year? It still leaves me with more than two million for myself."

"What you need," Janov told him, "is something that will *make* you scream. Between now and next week, see if you can find something and I'll work on it from my end, as well."

Lennon found it that very night, completely by accident. While changing stations on his hotel TV set he stopped at "The Merv Griffin Show." Sonny and Cher were on the screen, Cher singing her heart out, Sonny silent and stone-faced behind her. Lennon remembered them as teenybopper idols in America a few years earlier. They were on the downslide of their career (before their 1972 comeback).

Lennon turned around to Yoko. "That Cher has some voice. She's still got it, all right." Then something strange happened. Cher went silent, and Sonny began singing solo. Lennon instinctively covered his ears, but it was too late. All of a sudden, to both Yoko's and his own surprise, John began screaming, louder and harder than at any time since he sang "Money" onstage in Hamburg nearly ten years earlier. Yoko was terrified. So was Lennon, in fact, until he realized it was only his peculiar reaction to Sonny Bono's voice. He and Yoko both arrived at the same conclusion simultaneously. They were overjoyed.

"That's it!" Lennon exclaimed. "That's what I need! Sonny Bono! I've got to call the station."

He learned that this particular Griffin show had been taped two months earlier and that Sonny and Cher were currently working the lounge at the Flamingo Hotel in Las Vegas. He finally reached Bono there:

"Hello, Sonny. This is John Lennon."

"John Lennon?" said a startled Bono. *"Of the Beatles' John Lennon?"*

"Yes. Yes indeed. Yoko and I just saw you on 'The Merv Griffin Show' and you were great. We'd like you to visit us this weekend at the house we're going to rent here in L.A. Can you make it?"

"Make it? I'll leave now and walk if I have to! Wait'll I tell Cher! Here she is now. Cher! You'll never believe it. This is John Lennon on the phone and he wants us to come over to visit him and Yoko this weekend in L.A.!"

"John Lennon?" John heard Cher ask from the background. "Of the Beatles' John Lennon?"

"That's right, honey. I told you I'd get us back to the top." Then to Lennon: "Say when and where, John. We close out here tonight anyway."

"My aides will contact you and give you the complete details. See you soon, Sonny . . . oh, Sonny! Hold it! Don't hang up. Is it true—funny, all of a sudden I remember hearing this somewhere—that you have an enormous stockpile of Ipana toothpaste in your house? It is? Do you think maybe you could bring a couple of tubes with you? I'll make it worth your while . . ."

As he hung up, Lennon could hardly believe his good fortune. Primal screams whenever he wanted them *and* Ipana toothpaste!

Ringo Starr enjoyed one hit single after another in 1972. First there was Gallery's "It's So Nice to Be with You," then Melanie's "Candles in the Rain," John Denver's "Country Roads," and his favorite: Dylan's "Knockin' on Heaven's Door." [4] Even Ringo himself had another hit: "Only You." Ringo enjoyed still more hits after this before scoring with *his* next smash, "No No Song." [5] But

---

4. Any time you get tired of this joke, just raise your hand. I have others.
5. You can all put your hands down now, thank you.

after this one, the hits suddenly stopped. The albums continued—*Goodnight Vienna* and *Rotogravure* both sold respectably—but Ringo's momentum had collapsed. Ringo, however, was not one to brood or get stuck in the trap of trying to get a stalled career back on the track. There were always the movies, anyway. It seemed like the best direction to take at the time, and what did he have to lose? So he gave the movies a try. Ringo now feels it was a mistake, and regrets spending the entire year of 1975 running from theater to theater, watching a total of 784 movies, which he feels was detrimental to his music, his eyesight, and his intellect.

George Harrison was in trouble. Another album was due in two months and he still didn't have any new songs for it. He called Colin Owen for advice. After agreeing on a price, Owen offered his suggestions:

"Why not do an oldies album?"

"No! Absolutely not," Harrison vehemently protested. "They'd know I ran out of material if I did that."

"You're giving the public too much credit for intelligence. They wouldn't know—"

"Who's talking about the public?" Harrison interrupted. "I'm talking about John and Paul. I've got a pretty good shot at eternal life. What do I have to fear from the *public?* No, it's John and Paul I'm after."

"Well, in that case do a benefit concert for the starving children in Biafra, and release an album of the concert."

"A benefit concert," Harrison said slowly. "For Biafra . . . I need to think about it for a while. I'll call you back, Colin."

"Go ahead and think about it, George. I tell you it's a winner. I've always believed in this charity angle. People eat it up. How else do you explain a Jerry Lewis or a Danny Thomas? I think it's right for you, too."

Two hours later, Owen's phone rang. it was Harrison.

"I like it, Colin, and the more I think about it, the

more I like it. But let me ask you something. Are there starving children anywhere outside Biafra?"

The question caught Owen off guard, "Uh, I guess so . . . Why?"

"I'm working on a song for the concert and I need another syllable to make it scan. 'Biafra' only has three syllables. I need four. Think of another place."

Owen was silent. He'd read an article at the dentist's office a few weeks ago about a region hit by a drought . . . what was the name of it? Then he remembered: "Bangladesh! Would 'Bangladesh' work in your song?" he asked Harrison.

"Afraid not. Still has only three syllables. Need four."

"Well, *say* it differently. You're saying 'bon-gla-desh.' But you can add a syllable and who's going to know? Say 'bon-*gull*-a-desh' and see if that doesn't work. Go ahead, say it."

Harrison repeated this pronunciation several times, until he was satisfied.

"It works, Colin. It's perfect. I like the way it sounds, too. Real mysterious. 'Bon-*gull*-a-desh.' By the way, where is Bangladesh?"

"I don't know. Somewhere in India. Go to the library—"

"India!" Harrison couldn't believe his luck. "If it's India, I can use Shankar and all those cats, and the whole thing makes sense. The exposure'll be great for Ravi, too. He's been having a tough time of it with his sales in the States. He won't tour unless he's the top-billed act, and he isn't a big enough draw there to fill a decent-sized nightclub. This could do it for him!"

"Not to mention you, too, of course," Owen reminded him.

As they drove up the twisting road to the Lennons' rented home in Benedict Canyon, Sonny Bono told his wife, "This is the kind of break that doesn't come often in this business." The Bonos were prepared to make the most of it. An association with John Lennon would give them credibility with the same audience that had left them behind. This was one chance they were not going to blow.

John answered the doorbell himself. He shook Sonny's hand, kissed Cher's cheek and welcomed them inside to meet Yoko, who was immersed in the tarot cards she and John had been reading prior to the Bonos' arrival.

"What are those things?" Cher asked Yoko.

"These are the cards which reveal your future," Yoko said cryptically.

Sonny grabbed a handful, examined them, and scratched his head, somewhat puzzled.

"I've never seen anything like these," he told John.

"Aren't they big in America yet?" John asked. "Yoko and I have been into them for a month already."

"No," Sonny said, "the only thing we've got like it that I know about is baseball cards. You collect baseball cards? I've got the complete set for 1958, '59, and '61. In fact," Sonny continued, picking up momentum, "I've got *doubles* on the famous Ted Williams misprint card that had him playing third base for the Yankees! You believe that? I also got doubles on Pee Wee Ree—"

"*Sonny!*" Cher could see she was going to have to watch him all the time.

"Did you bring the Ipana, Sonny?" John asked. "I've been telling Yoko about it for months. Can't find it anywhere nowadays."

"Sure. Cher's got it in her purse."

"No I don't, Sonny," Cher informed him. "Don't you remember? You told me not to bring the tubes I had, that you were gonna get a full case from upstairs?"

Sonny smacked himself on his forehead with the heel of his right hand, in the classic Italian gesture of dismay. Yoko was unfamiliar with the custom.

"Why do you hit yourself like that, Sonny Bono?" she asked.

"Because he's an idiot!" Cher answered for him. "How

could you be so *stupid?*" she chided Sonny. She was so angry she forgot everything else. "Three thousand tubes of that goddamned Ipana toothpaste that nobody but an idiot like you would stockpile. If a *beggar* wanted them, you ought to be glad to give them away. But a *Beatle* wants them, for God's sake! We're working three shows a night for a bunch of drunks who sit there and stare at my ass the entire show and we finally get the break of a lifetime and you forget the stupid toothpaste—"

Lennon stopped her. "Cher! Cher! Calm down now. Everything's all right." She's about to pull a Donovan, Lennon thought. "I've waited this long for the Ipana, I can wait a bit longer. You think this is the last time we're going to see each other? We want to see a *lot* of you two."

Sonny beamed. He liked Lennon so much he was even considering letting him have the emergency tube of Ipana he kept tucked under the seat of his car.

"I haven't heard any of your songs for quite a while," John said. "You two still recording?"

"No, not much. Looking for the right producer." Cher was confident Lennon would never discover the lie. Since nobody else had heard the singles they'd been releasing every two months since their last hit, it was unlikely that Lennon had heard them either.

"Both Cher and I have been big Beatle fans since the beginning," Sonny said perfunctorily, "and it was really a sad day for music when you guys called it quits—"

Lennon was quite sick of *that* line. If he and Sonny were going to be spending a considerable amount of time together, he wanted it understood.

"On the contrary, Sonny," Lennon said firmly. "It was a *great* day for music. Let me tell you something: I don't believe in I Ching! I don't believe in Yoga! I don't believe in Krishna! I don't believe in Mantra! I don't believe in Zimmerman! And I don't believe in *the Beatles!* I just believe in me. Yoko and me! And that's reality!"

Sonny held both hands in front of his face, "Okay,

John! Okay! No need to get steamed about anything. We never really liked the Beatles that much anyway, did we Cher?"

Cher looked at both John and her husband, and said, "Who's 'Zimmerman'?"

Mixing drinks in the kitchen, John put his arms around Yoko and whispered into her ear: "Isn't it wonderful? He hasn't even started singing and already he's aggravating the hell out of me!"

Within weeks the Bonos were spending so much time with the Lennons that they'd practically moved in. Sonny was only too happy to oblige John when he needed to scream. Just a few bars of his 1965 solo hit "Laugh at Me" were enough to keep Lennon screaming until he was hoarse and blue in the face. And Yoko and Cher were hitting it off splendidly—shopping, cooking, taking in an occasional movie.

"It's what she always needed," John told Sonny one afternoon. "Somebody to hang around with. Another female, you know, someone to talk to."

As for Sonny, he was delighted. The current issue of *Rolling Stone* had a huge picture of Cher and Yoko squeezing tomatoes at the Hollywood Safeway super-market. The story told of the affinity which the Lennons had for the Bonos, and a companion picture of Bono's entire Ipana toothpaste stash (transferred by now to Lennon's house) did him no harm either. The whole idea of stockpiling a discontinued brand of toothpaste seemed so irresistibly hip that an entire new Ipana cult sprang up among the trend-setters on both coasts, inflating the price of a tube of regular Ipana up to $85. (Spearmint went up to $100 a tube!)

Sonny had succeeded beyond his wildest expectations. Still, something was troubling him, holding him back from complete fulfillment. For days he tried to identify the source of his discomfort. The answer came to him in his sleep. He woke Cher up and told her. She understood, but felt his plan was too risky. Why rock the boat?

Sonny disagreed: "You think Ed Sullivan would be where he is today if he was afraid to take a chance?"

"Ed Sullivan wouldn't be where he is today, if he had taken it a little easier," Cher said. "He died last week, Sonny."

"I'm still not happy, Cher. I'm talking to John about it tomorrow."

Over a breakfast of Post Toasties and Instant Karma ("Good stuff," Yoko told Cher, "much better than Nestle's Quik") Sonny informed Lennon he was unhappy. Lennon was genuinely concerned. For apart from Sonny's help with the primal screaming, and apart from his Ipana stash—apart from all of that—John *liked* Sonny. He was a likeable guy. What was the problem?

"I'm a performer, John. I've always been a performer. I need an audience. I need to hear that applause. I miss it. I even miss those stinking Vegas lounges we were working before we met you and Yoko—that's how much I miss an audience."

"Hmm. I see," Lennon said, looking deep into his Post Toasties. He remained silent for a minute or so. Sonny and Cher were both afraid they'd offended him. Finally, a telephone call snapped Lennon out of his trance. When he returned five minutes later, his face was alive with excitement.

"Cher! Sonny!" he said enthusiastically, shifting his gaze from one to the other. "How'd you like to join Yoko and myself onstage at a rock & roll revival show in Toronto?"

It was too much for Sonny to believe.

"You mean Cher and I performing as part of your band?" He said the words slowly, trying to delay as long as possible the moment when Lennon would surely tell him it was just a joke.

"No, Sonny. Not as a *part* of our band. As the band!

You and me and Cher and Yoko! We've got three weeks to rehearse, and I know all those old songs already. You know them too, for that matter."

"Wh-who's gonna play the instruments?"

"Oh, don't worry about that. I'll play guitar, and I can always get Eric Clapton or someone on lead. In fact, I can get anyone I want as backup musicians. With the exception, possibly, of Paul McCartney."

Sonny and Cher looked at each other. Their comeback was complete and they knew it. John was happy for both of them.

The one misgiving John had about the whole project was Sonny's voice—he was afraid it might start him screaming uncontrollably in the middle of the concert. Such fears were laid to rest at the rehearsal that afternoon. Lennon learned that Sonny's singing only affected him when Sonny sang unaccompanied. When he sang with Cher or even with the background music from the old records they were using at rehearsal, he had no effect on Lennon whatsoever. Sonny found this information fascinating, and promised never to sing unaccompanied unless Lennon specifically requested it.

Three weeks later John and Yoko and Sonny and Cher huddled nervously backstage at Toronto's Maple Leaf Gardens awaiting the announcement that for them would culminate three weeks of intense preparation:

"Ladies and Gentlemen! The group you've all been waiting for: *The Plastic Bono Band!*"

22

Slow Down

From the control booth at the Abbey Road recording studio, Paul McCartney could barely be seen behind the massive drum kit he was playing. Giant headphones—inside them the music he himself had made earlier and was now providing the percussion for—obscured his face. Linda McCartney was the only other person (except for the engineer) in the studio that afternoon. She was in the midst of taking what seemed like hundreds of pictures of her husband in the process of recording. When Paul finished the drum track, he motioned the engineer to play back the full song over the huge monitors. Halfway through the playback, McCartney stood up and began waving his hands over his head, a signal to the engineer to stop the tape. The engineer's voice came booming through the speakers:

"What's the matter, Paul? Drums mixed too loud?"

"No, no. Everything's fine. I want to talk to Linda for a few minutes. Why don't you knock off for lunch?"

When they were alone, Linda McCartney poured her husband a cup of tea and sat across from him at a table in the middle of the studio. Paul was dissatisfied. She was sure of it.

"What's wrong, honey?"

"It's been three years now, Linda, and it's still not coming out the way I like it," Paul told her. Linda, like any good wife, provided reassurance.

"Nonsense, Paul. You're making the best music of your life."

"Music?" McCartney asked. "Who said anything about music? It's your tea. It stinks and I'm getting tired of it! At first I made allowances. She's American, I told myself. What could she know about tea? Give her time, she'll learn. But you haven't learned, Linda. After three years, you still make the worst cup of tea in London! If you spent half as much time learning how to brew a decent cup as you do squinting into that camera—"

Linda started crying. McCartney apologized.

"I'm sorry, honey. It's not your tea. It never was. It's my music. I've done three albums now, played every instrument myself on all of them, and frankly, I miss being in a band."

Linda looked up. "A band?" she said sobbing. "You want to start up the Beatles again?"

"No, of course not," McCartney said adamantly. "Absolutely not. No way. After they rejected your dad, no way in the world."

"But who would you get to join your band?"

"I don't care, Linda. Anybody. Just some musicians I respect. Doesn't matter *who* so long as they're good. You don't know how tough it is working all by yourself. There's no feedback. You never know if your ideas are good or if they're bullshit."

"Your ideas are always good, Paul."

"That's exactly what I mean, honey. Anyone who has a lot of ideas has their share of great ones and their share of bullshit ones. That's the one thing I appreciated about working with John. He was never afraid to tell me when a particular idea of mine was bullshit, and I did the same for him. You don't know how valuable that is to an artist. It's downright *necessary*, and that's why I'm putting together a band."

The band McCartney formed, Wings, was made up of former Moody Blues member Denny Laine, guitarist Jimmy McCulloch, drummer Joe English, and, of course,

Paul and Linda McCartney. Tremendous musicians, they provided McCartney with the muscle his songs needed, and as a working unit, allowed McCartney to tour—an advantage the other ex-Beatles lacked.

As you can imagine, finding musicians of the caliber of Laine, McCulloch, and English was a difficult task. McCartney personally auditioned more than forty· guitarists, for example, before settling on McCulloch. Interestingly, Paul was more impressed with another guitarist, Eric Cambridge, former lead guitarist of Noel Redding's group, Fat Mattress, and only an argument during the audition prevented Cambridge from becoming Wings' guitarist. Cambridge tells the story in his book[1]:

> Paul was pleased with me, I could tell. He told me I'd played rings around all the other guitarists he'd auditioned, and that I was miles ahead of George Harrison, as well. I figured I was home free and started thinking about what color Rolls Royce I should get. I mean, I was that certain. Then the roof fell in. Paul asked me to work out a lead part for a new song he'd written. But the song was . . . well . . . *weak,* to put it charitably. I could no more have hung a guitar part on that flimsy melody than you could have hung an elephant on a clothesline. I told him so—politely, of course. He started laughing. "You mean it's bullshit," he said. I thought, "Wow, what a down-to-earth cat." I'd had him pegged as all-ego up to then. "Yeah," I said, "it's kind of bullshit." Then he said, "Who the hell are *you* to tell *me* my songs are bullshit? You're fired!"

For George Harrison the Bangladesh concert was the supreme moment of his life. Madison Square Garden. Instant sellout. Onstage with the likes of Bob Dylan, Eric

---

1. *Flying Without Wings,* Eric Cambridge (Sour Grapes Press, 1974).

Clapton, Leon Russell, even Klaus Voormann. He was making history, feeding hungry children, and fulfilling his contractual requirements all at the same time. He wanted the night to last forever.

But it didn't, and one year later the greatest humanitarian event in rock history was only a memory and a new album was due. Once again, it was the same old problem: no material. Painfully, he searched himself for inspiration. Nothing came to him. He sought the advice of Ravi Shankar, who told him to stop looking within himself, that there was "a whole world of material" out there. Inspired, he started to write. The songs were by no means great, but at least they were songs. "Give Me Love, Give Me Peace on Earth" was perhaps the best of the lot, and was released as a single. In his most plaintive voice, Harrison asked for love, for peace on earth, and for hope to cope with his heavy load.

America was overcome with sympathy for Harrison, and the single shot up into the Top Ten in a matter of weeks. Radio stations asked listeners to send cards and letters to Harrison to cheer him up, a group of starving musicians in Bangladesh planned a benefit for him "to help him cope with his heavy load," as they phrased it. It was a wonderful display. The album, *Living in the Material World*, was released quickly afterward to capitalize on the sympathy campaign already underway, but instead brought it skidding to a halt. It was, simply, a terrible album and those who had been busy feeling sorry for Harrison before were now feeling sorry for themselves for buying it.

The Plastic Bono Band was a smash in Toronto and on the flight back to L.A. Lennon was already talking to Sonny and Cher about doing an album. But Lennon had been beaten to the punch by a representative of the CBS television network, who offered the pair a weekly show on the network. They jumped at the opportunity.

Lennon was furious. He felt used and taken advantage

of. To this day, he refuses to allow the name "Sonny Bono" to be uttered in his presence and hasn't brushed with Ipana in years. "I'll even use *Ultra-Brite* before I use the same toothpaste as Sonny Bono," he told friends afterward.

Bitter, hurt, and defeated, he used his first solo album *John Lennon—Plastic Ono Band* (dropping the "B" in Bono to erase any reference to Sonny) to vent his hostilities at Sonny and Cher. The album was painful to listen to, being so forthright, so candid, so brutally honest, and so poorly sung. Songs such as "I Found Out" cut no corners when it came to frankness:

> Found you in Vegas
> And we became friends
> Only to watch you use me
> To achieve your selfish ends.
>
> I thought we were a team
> Nobody but you could make me scream
> But like a toothpaste tube you squeezed me dry
> And left me here to sit and cry.
>
> Yes, I found out.
> I found out
> What you're all about.

Lennon, as bitter as anyone had ever seen him, took every step he could to damage Sonny and Cher's career, culminating in sending a letter to every radio station in the U.S. The letter forbade stations to play any John Lennon record if they were also playing Sonny and Cher's "A Cowboy's Work Is Never Done," the duo's hit single at the time. If a single letter had ever come close to destroying a career, surely it was this one. It was more than a year before any American radio station played another John Lennon song.

By 1976, Ringo Starr was no longer enjoying hit records with the same sort of regularity that he had in the early '70s. An occasional record appealed to him, like Elton John's "Philadelphia Freedom," but by and large, he found little to enjoy. Perhaps his negative opinion of the music scene was due to his own lack of success on the charts. Not being a songwriter, he was forced to rely on the tunes of others, and the material he was getting was, frankly, dismal.

After his 1975 single "Goodnight Vienna" flopped miserably he revealed to *Rolling Stone* that he hated the song and didn't believe it was ever a hit in the first place. "Who's going to hit the Top Ten with a song about saying goodnight to a town in Germany?" he said in an interview. The follow-up, "A Dose of Rock & Roll," fared slightly better, but once again the lyrics kept the buyers away. The song's claim that rock & roll was the cure for every ailment, was unconvincing and somehow left the listener with a vague feeling of depression after hearing it:

> If your parents die
> Or your wife's taken up with another man
> And left you in the cold
> Try a dose of rock & roll!
>
> If you lose your job
> And can't get another because you're too old
> Don't worry at all just
> Try a dose of rock & roll!

With his recording career a failure, Ringo made one last bold move: he cut off all his hair. But it didn't help and, in retrospect, it's hard to see how it could have. Despondent, he divorced his wife, remarried, and shut himself off from the world by staying inside his house in the Hollywood Hills, watching Gene Autry movies with his new wife. But as his new wife only appeared in two Gene Autry movies, he soon grew bored. Movie offers came every week—from Harry Nilsson, Alice Cooper, and all the rest of Ringo's Hollywood pals—but Ringo was in no mood to go to the movies. Although only in his early thirties, he nonetheless felt as though his life had already been lived. He lost interest in everything, and even gave his fabled rings away to former Monkee Mickey Dolenz in return for Dolenz's promise that he wouldn't come over anymore. But nothing helped.

Then one morning in April 1978 he awoke early and realized what he needed. He woke his wife and told her.

"I realize what I need," he whispered in her ear.

"What is it, darling?" she asked.

"A cup of coffee. Two sugars. No cream."

"And for that you woke me up?" she asked angrily. "When did you become crippled?"

"I'm sorry. Dunno why I expected you to get it for me. Just used to that sort of treatment, I guess being a Beatle and all—"

"A Beatle? You aren't a Beatle! Eight years ago you might have been a Beatle, but we've got a thing called the Statute of Limitations in this country, and it's run out for you. Get your own coffee!"

For Ringo Starr, standing barefoot on the cold kitchen linoleum at 7 A.M. that April morning, it was a revelation. Now he knew. He wanted to be a Beatle again.

Eric Cambridge, the would-be Wings guitarist, revealed in his book *Flying Without Wings* that McCartney had a quite different impression of his own music than most other listeners did:

"He thought the songs he was writing were *heavy*, and I don't mean just lyrically—he thought the music itself was powerful, and that people only felt it was lightweight because the English studios he was using made *everything* sound lightweight. I told him groups like Led Zeppelin and Deep Purple managed to get a heavy sound in English studios. He asked me if I was accusing him of 'bullshit' which I was, but I denied it. If only I'd denied it the *other* time he asked me, I'd be *owning* the silver Rolls Royce I drive every day, instead of chauffeuring Bernie Taupin in it . . ."

It was this dissatisfaction with Britain's studio facilities that led McCartney to choose Africa as the site of his next recording. The other members of Wings were somewhat less than delighted about going all the way to Africa, but agreed without hesitation. As one member put it later, "Saying no to Paul McCartney was like saying no to a million dollars. *Just* like it, in fact . . ."

McCartney had trouble finding a studio in Africa that would record him. Most studios kicked the group out while they were putting down the backing tracks, even before the vocals were added. A McCartney aide, Malcolm Tent, recalls a typical experience:

> Paul and Joe [English, Wings' drummer] were recording the rhythm track to "Mrs. Vanderbilt" when suddenly the two African engineers in the control booth started banging on the glass. Really *banging* on it, I mean. Paul figured they were just getting into the rhythm, and didn't pay any attention, continuing to play his bass, lost in the music in his headphones. All of a sudden this voice comes booming into the studio through the monitors and into Paul's headphones. *"What is that crap, man?"* it said. *"I just had breakfast. You can't come in here and play like that . . ."* We had to pack up and move on to the next town, where the same thing happened. Luckily, in Lagos, Nigeria—after being chased out of studios in eleven African nations—we found one owned by a distant African relative of Brian Epstein's. He didn't like the music any better than the others, but allowed us to do the LP there in memory of "his dear cousin Brian," as he put it . . . [2]

The resulting album, *Band on the Run,* took its name

2. From the collection, *People Who in Any Way Had Something to Do with the Beatles* (U. Zuckers, Vellvoret & Howe, 1975).

from Wings' African experience and, surprisingly, backs
up McCartney's claim that his music could sound stronger
if it was recorded away from Britain. It was his best all-
around album, and probably the best of all the solo Beatle
efforts. The record went platinum only weeks after it first
hit the stores [3] and it looked as if with Wings, Mc-
Cartney's solo potential would finally be realized.

With the next album, however, problems arrived for
McCartney. His desire to return to Lagos was thwarted by
his wife, who felt the country was uncivilized, since you
couldn't find either L'Eggs' "Sheer Energy" pantyhose or
Sara Lee cheesecake *anywhere* in Nigeria, let alone Lagos.
McCartney considered leaving her behind, but Linda had
developed into such a brilliant keyboard player by this
time that Wings simply couldn't do without her. So *Venus
& Mars* ("We wanted to do a spacy kind of album,"
McCartney told *New Musical Express*) was recorded in
England, and the same old problems crept in. Critics
branded it "flimsy, lightweight, and soppy" and dismissed
it.[4] *Venus & Mars* was not without its good moments,
however. The moment between the end of "Love in Song"
and the beginning of the next cut, "You Gave Me the
Answer," was tolerable, and there were several similar
moments on both sides of the record.

Disregarding the critical assault on *Venus & Mars*,
McCartney plunged ahead, planning both a new album
and an American tour. It was to be his first appearance on

3. Due to a problem with the vinyl, corrected in later pressings. The estimated
20,000 platinum copies are now collectors' items, the worth of which is rivaled
among Beatle enthusiasts only by McCartney's original pre-Beatle album, the
original *Meat* LP cover, and the extremely rare "From Me to You" B-side,
"Introducing the Beatles," on Swan Records. This B-side appeared only on the
DJ/Promotional copies of the single, not on the copies sold to consumers.
4. Copies of *Venus & Mars* with "Flimsy, Lightweight, & Soppy" branded on
them have become valuable collectors' items among Beatle enthusiasts. In a
recent collectors' auction, one rabid Beatlemaniac offered both his copy of
McCartney's pre-Beatle album *and* any one member of his family in trade for
the branded *Venus & Mars*.

a U.S. stage since the Beatles' 1966 show at Los Angeles' Dodger Stadium.[5]

In the ensuing months, McCartney and Wings worked tirelessly, setting up the tour and finishing the new album, *Wings at the Speed of Sound.* Then—only days before the first American concert—a bombshell was dropped that threatened the entire tour: Linda McCartney announced she was leaving Wings to join the American band Steely Dan.

Despite devoting his first-ever solo album, *John Lennon—Plastic Ono Band,* to his bitter experience with Sonny and Cher, it still failed to relieve Lennon's hostility over the whole affair. And as Sonny and Cher's weekly variety show climbed higher and higher in the ratings, Lennon's distaste for them grew until it became an intense hatred for everything they represented—Hollywood, money, Chastity, the entire show-business establishment, etc.

Lennon's first move was to abandon Hollywood for New York City, where at least the tinseled glamour would be absent. In New York, he met political activist Abbie Hoffman in the elevator at the Waldorf-Astoria. Hoffman, an embittered radical (and one of the few remaining radicals anywhere in America in early 1973), was also a born salesman. By the time the elevator had reached the twentieth floor, he'd convinced John and Yoko to throw their support behind his radical causes. (To be completely fair, Lennon did have a moment of hesitation between the eighth and twelfth floors, but Hoffman overcame it by the sixteenth.)

Lennon invited Hoffman to join them for lunch in the Waldorf's dining room to discuss their place in the movement. Hoffman, patiently explaining that the Wal-

5. Technically, the final Beatle performance was the following night at San Francisco's Cow Palace. Since the audience for this show consisted entirely of farm animals, most Beatle historians don't count it.

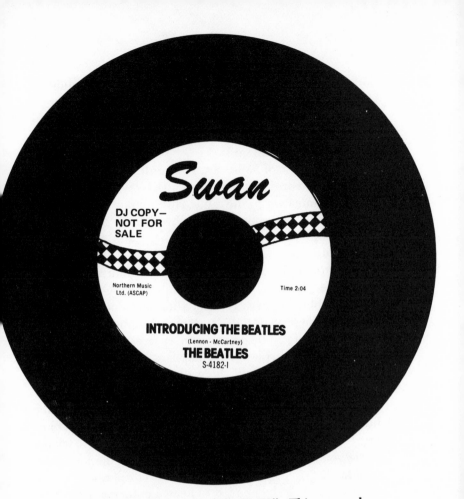

"INTRODUCING THE BEATLES"—This song only
appeared on the B-side of DJ copies of
"From Me To You" (commercial copies had another
song, "Ask Me Why," as a flipside).
"Introducing The Beatles" is an early example of the
Beatles' unpretentious sense of humor. Over
a rocking Chuck Berry-style riff, Ringo's voice cuts
through: "JOHN, THIS IS PAUL." Lennon
responds: "NICE TO MEET YOU, PAUL, THIS IS
GEORGE." Harrison replies: "NICE TO
MEET YOU, PAUL. I'D LIKE YOU TO MEET
RINGO . . ." and on and on for 2:04. One of
the rarest of all Beatle sides.

dorf-Astoria was no place to discuss radical activities, suggested the House of Pancakes on 34th Street instead. Yoko was delighted. She had been a cook there once, she told Hoffman.

"Who cares?" he said.

At the House of Pancakes, Yoko ordered for everyone— chocolate silver-dollar pancakes. The owner recognized her, and came over to the table. He congratulated Yoko on her recent work, especially her "bag-ism" ("Bagging John Lennon was nice work," he told her), and explained to John how much she had been missed.

"Yoko could do things with cheese blintzes that still amaze me," he said. "Once in a while, she'd come up with a cheese blintz that was such a masterpiece, I wouldn't allow it to be served to the customer. I'd pin it to that wall over there," he said, pointing to an area near the coffee machine, "and display it for her fans. In fact, I just took her last cheese blintz off the wall a few months ago."

Yoko looked disappointed.

"Well, Yoko, come on," he said apologetically. "That blintz had been up there since 1961. The Health Department was getting on my back about it. Tell you what— while you're waiting for your pancakes, I'd be honored if you'd make us another cheese blintz to display—"

That was all she needed to hear. Lennon and Hoffman didn't see her again until they'd finished eating. Their conversation was overheard by Chinese bus boy Kit Chan, who openly admitted his eavesdropping, and said he listened in on everybody else in the place as well. ("I could tell you stories about that new girl behind the counter that would fly your hair . . .") Chan's recollection of the famous Lennon-Hoffman exchange:

"The problem, John, which you may or may not be aware of, is that ninety percent of the wealth in this country—in the *world* in fact—is controlled by only ten percent of the people."

Hoffman waited for a reaction. Lennon didn't provide one. Hoffman continued: "Now we don't want to take it all away from them. We just want to *redistribute* it equally so that everyone has their fair share."

"You're a good talker, Abbie," Lennon said, "but you've got some job ahead of you convincing the fat cats to—what was the word?—"

"Redistribute."

". . . to redistribute their wealth. How do you intend to do it?"

Hoffman expected this question. After all, he'd heard it hundreds of times by now.

"By any means necessary, John."

"Up to and including violent overthrow of the United States government?" asked an uneasy Lennon.

"Sure, if we could. But we can't. Not violence. I'm not against it in principle, only in action. I mean, on their side you've got the biggest military arsenal in the world, and on our side, what've you got? A handful of radicals. And radicals can't fight, that's for sure. Ever see a radical fight? They can't even throw a baseball right. They throw it like a girl does—you know, with their elbow instead of their shoulder—"

"Well, wait a minute, Abbie," Lennon interrupted, "What's your plan, then?"

"It's simple and it'll work. I want to communicate to the people—and I mean the *people*—in a language the pigs can't understand. And the language is *music.*"

Lennon was impressed.

"I want this music to be *your* music, John," he continued, his voice taking on evangelistic overtones. "Think of it! Instead of just writing songs and making records to please yourself, you can now do it and make the world a better place to live in for everybody! It'll give you a *reason* to create, the best reason of all: *for your fellow man!"* [6]

Lennon was sold. Within weeks, Hoffman and fellow

6. From *Sticky Fingers—Cleaning Up the Food of the Stars* by Kit Chan (Syrupticious Publications, 1974).

radical Jerry Rubin had found a backup band of street radicals called Elephant's Memory, and Lennon's radical phase was underway.

Lennon and Elephant's Memory made their debut outside the Michigan State Prison to benefit John Sinclair (a father figure in the Michigan radical movement). Sinclair was serving a one-to-ten year sentence, ostensibly for drug possession, but Hoffman, Rubin and others in radical circles believed he was actually being persecuted for his bad poetry. Lennon first read Sinclair's poetry at Rubin's apartment and it had an immediate and profound effect on the newly radicalized ex-Beatle. After he returned from the bathroom, he agreed to do the benefit, provided that he would never be forced to read any more of Sinclair's work.

Elephant's Memory was a dynamic hard-rock band, the perfect backup for Lennon, always a rocker at heart. He liked working with them and respected their radical convictions so much that he decided to use the group on his next album. ("Sure, I could get Ry Cooder and Billy Preston and Nicky Hopkins, and all the rest, but what do they know about Mao or socialist collectivism?" he told interviewers from *Rolling Stone*.)

A double album was planned, but Lennon and Elephant's Memory had a falling-out halfway through the project. Elephant's Memory wanted a royalty rate of 4.25 percent on the first 100,000 copies sold, accelerating to 4.75 percent on everything from 100,000 to 500,000, and a flat 5 percent on everything exceeding that. Lennon agreed to these demands, but Elephant's Memory then insisted on getting residuals on any future re-packaging of the album, including that of the lucrative TV mail-order variety (such as K-Tel, etc.). When Lennon refused, they threatened to bring Lee Eastman in to negotiate. With this, Lennon exploded:

"What is all this crap? What about Mao? What about Karl Marx? What about—"

He couldn't even finish his outburst before Elephant's Memory returned his volley:

"What about the payments on my Benz?" asked one.

"What about my Park Avenue apartment?" demanded another.

"What about my coke dealer?" screamed a third.

Lennon, by now thoroughly disgusted, withdrew from the radical movement completely and began referring to his former compatriots as hypocrites. He disappeared for a few weeks, then turned up to perform with Yoko at Frank Zappa's Fillmore East Concert. The live recording of this performance plus the Elephant's Memory studio tracks made up *Sometime in New York City,* Lennon's new album. Onstage at the Fillmore, Yoko (hidden inside a white bag) hovered at Lennon's feet, and almost suffered a severe injury when a member of Zappa's band—thinking the bag was something thrown onstage—tried to kick it back into the audience. Fortunately, he was stopped in time.

23

If I Needed Someone

After being fired for selling promotional albums to record stores, Warner Brothers Records executive Bernie "Bullets" Birnbaum wrote a sizzling expose of the record industry.[1] In it, he describes the moment when George Harrison decided to abandon his solo career. Although Birnbaum's credibility is suspect, it nonetheless makes for interesting speculation:

> It was during the playback of a song he'd written for his 33 1/3 album, "Crackerbox Palace." I was in the studio waiting for a break to come so I could introduce A. Pauling Taist [*the most powerful and influential radio programmer in America*] to George. After the playback, Harrison turned to both of us and said, "That's not only the most pointless song I've ever written, it's the most pointless song *anyone's* ever written. I don't know what a 'crackerbox palace' is! Imagine that! I wrote it and sang it and I don't even know what it is! It doesn't mean a thing to me. I can't deny it any longer—I'm all tapped out. I must be . . . sheesh! "Crackerbox Palace!" What am I gonna follow that with? *Pretzel Mansion?*"

1. *Lunch Is My Business—Confessions of a Record Biz Exec* by Bernard "Bullets" Birnbaum (Imp Press, 1977).

Paul McCartney was frantic. At first he thought Linda was kidding about joining Steely Dan, but now he knew she meant it.

"I'm a musician, Paul," his wife told him at breakfast two days before the American tour was set to begin. "You seem to forget that."

"That's not true, honey. You get in plenty of licks on our LPs, you get recognition—"

"*Recognition!* Don't make me laugh. Recognition!" She pointed at McCartney, but turned her head away from him and continued talking, addressing herself now to an imaginary third person:

"You *believe* this?" she asked the imaginary person. "He throws me a bone every other album like that 'Queen of the House' crap, and he calls that *participating*. Now I get a chance to join *Steely Dan,* my favorite group in the whole world, and he's gonna tell me I shouldn't do it?"

"But Linda," McCartney pleaded, "you're my *wife.* Doesn't that mean anything to you?"

Linda continued her conversation with the imaginary third person.

"Oh, *now* I'm his *wife.* That's what it finally comes down to, isn't it? He doesn't think I'm capable of carrying on a career as keyboard player of Steely Dan and being his wife at the same time. Yet, of course, *he* can be the leader of Wings and still be my *husband.* Have you ever heard such a double standard? Will somebody please tell my provincial husband that we're living in *1978* not *1948*?"

Paul could see that any continuation of this argument would only make a solution that much more difficult. He tried another approach:

"What's it gonna take for you to stay in the group, Linda?"

"Top billing."

"*What?*"

"You heard me. Top billing."

"You mean *Linda McCartney and Wings*?" Paul could hardly say it without choking.

"Yes. *Linda McCartney and Wings.* What's so bad about that? We're a partnership. You've had top billing all these years, haven't you? What's so bad about me having it for a year or two? If your ego is going to be damaged, we can call it *Linda McCartney and Wings, Featuring Paul McCartney,* although we'd have to make the backstage passes bigger, to fit the whole name on there—"

"I won't hear of it! How would it look to the others? Lennon would laugh me out of the country—"

"*That's* what you care about, isn't it, Paul?" Linda said, seizing Paul's instinctive response. "You don't care about *my* opinion, or Denny's, or Joe's, or Jimmy's. You're still worrying about John Lennon, and George, and Ringo!"

"Well, I, uh . . ."

"Face it. It's true and you know it. I've *always* known it. Why do you think I took the offer from Steely Dan, anyway? Not because I want to leave Wings, but because I know there isn't gonna *be* any Wings next year at this time. And you know it too, don't you?"

"Well, I, uh . . ."

"Don't you?"

Paul was silent for a full minute, then surprised himself with his next statement:

"Yes, you're right," he said slowly, the words coming out by themselves. "I'm a Beatle. I'll always be a Beatle. I guess it's a lifetime membership."

Linda's tone softened until she became almost another woman—the same woman, in fact, that McCartney had always known her to be until these last few days.

"I'm doing our tour, honey," she said, "and I haven't even made up my mind about this Steely Dan business. And of course, it's *Paul McCartney and Wings.* It never was, and it couldn't be, anything else."

Paul looked at his wife through watery eyes. "Then why put me through all this?"

"I had to. I had to get you to admit to yourself what I

already knew and what you already knew inside. Other people besides yourself are involved here. There's me, and Joe, and Denny, and Jimmy, and our staff. They've got a right to plan their own futures, too."

"You're right," Paul agreed, "but let's keep it to ourselves for a while, at least till the tour's over. They're under contract to me for one more album, and I don't want them doing it with one eye on the classifieds. And I haven't even spoken to John or the others yet, so I really don't know where they're at."

"They'll be with you. They'll want to start the Beatles again." Linda said this with so much assurance her husband wondered if she knew something he didn't.

"How can you be so sure? Have you spoken with them?"

"No. But I *have* heard their albums."

If you had to reduce the solo careers of the Beatles to one word, "aimless" would probably be an accurate one. Such was John Lennon's plight in 1974. His *Sometime in New York City* album was so poorly received that many (to this day) feel it was an elaborate joke, some sort of ultimate put-on. But Lennon was serious, and the abuse hurt ("I'm like a journalist, reporting on my life, and that album was what was going on in my life at the time," he told reporters).

Plagued by marital difficulties and career indecision, he returned to Hollywood, alone, and stayed at record producer Lou Adler's house for six months until Adler came back from Europe.[2] For Lennon, it meant he could, after months of frantic running around, finally settle down. He attempted to write songs for his next album, but the songs just weren't coming.

Bored and depressed, he began hanging out with Harry

2. At which time a surprised Adler kicked him out. "I didn't even know him," he told reporters later.

Nilsson, a friend of Lennon shared with fellow ex-Beatle Ringo Starr.[3] Lennon was drinking heavily during this period, friends close to him claim (who say the closer they got to him, the more obvious it became). Lennon himself remembers waking up in unfamiliar surroundings (elevators; telephone booths; Duluth, Minnesota; etc.).

The culmination of this reckless period came one night at a widely reported incident at The Troubadour, a nightclub in West Los Angeles. Lennon and Nilsson were reportedly inebriated and while sitting in the audience began hurling insults at the Smothers Brothers. Their aim, altered by the alcohol, caused several of these insults to miss the Smothers Brothers and strike members of the audience instead. Aiming an insult at Tommy Smothers, Lennon instead hit Troubadour owner (and well-known local celebrity in her own right) "Two-Drink Minnie" Mumm, ruining her brand-new pantsuit. Furious, Minnie ejected the pair from the club, but not before Lennon had taped a Kotex sanitary napkin to his head.[4] At least a dozen photographers got pictures of the scene and they appeared in magazines and newspapers worldwide soon after. The incident was the subject of considerable controversy, many feeling it was in the poorest of taste,[5] many others believing (and rightfully so) that it was an incorrect use of a Kotex.

After the Troubadour incident, many of Lennon's old

3. Lennon got him on Mondays and weekends, Ringo on Thursdays and Fridays. Authorities are still trying to determine Nilsson's whereabouts on Tuesdays and Wednesdays.

4. The original Kotex pad used by Lennon that night is now a valuable collector's item. It was recovered outside The Troubadour by Cher Cropper (no relation to well-known studio musician Steve Cropper, as erroneously reported elsewhere), who has refused offers as high as $50,000 for the famous feminine napkin.

5. Troubadour owner Mumm was so offended by the entire Kotex incident that she established a policy of forbidding *anyone* to carry feminine hygiene products into the nightclub. Periodic attendance lulls caused her to abandon this policy, however.

friends began exhibiting concern about his state of mind. Phil Spector was one of them. Having bailed Lennon and the rest of the Beatles out of a jam at the time of their break-up, he once again came to the rescue. He called Lennon at Adler's house.

"John? This is Phil. I called to asked if everything was . . . you know . . . okay with you."

"Sure," Lennon said. "Everything's fine. Why?"

"Well, I just got through reading about that scene at The Troubadour . . ."

It was the final straw. Lennon exploded: "*What is it with everybody?* Can't a guy get drunk one night and let off a little steam without all his friends thinking he's gone off his rocker?"

Spector was sympathetic. "Hey, John, you don't have to explain anything to me. I understand. In fact, if I couldn't relate to the kind of pain a genius like you has to live with every day, I would have thought that whole Troubadour story was made up by the press."

Lennon appreciated Spector's empathy. "No, Phil, they didn't make that one up. I actually did it," he admitted. "Now I'm so embarrassed. I don't know what got into me."

"Forget it, John." Spector was reassuring. "Look at it like this—guys like you and me, we're extra *sensitive*. We receive so many impressions because of our sensitivity that sometimes we overload and go a little crazy."

"Really?"

"Sure," Spector continued, picking up momentum. "Most people are like TV sets that only get three channels, you know, like 2, 4, and 7. But guys like you and me, we get 2, 4, 7, 11, 28, 52—all of 'em, and sometimes it's just too much."

Lennon laughed. "That's a good way to put it, Phil. It's like our diagonal hold goes haywire, right?"

"Sure, that's all, John. Nothing that can't be repaired. In fact, you can repair it yourself."

"How?"

"*Work,*" Spector said with assurance. "You need to work, and I'll help you. I've rented Gold Star Studios tonight and I'd like to see you get something down on tape and forget about all this other nonsense."

"I'd really like that. You don't know how much I'd like that, Phil. But I have to confess something, and it *has* to stay between you and me."

"Anything. Have you ever known me to gossip?"

"Yes, and that's why I want your word on this. I don't want it on the streets."

"Word of honor. Don't worry."

There was a momentary silence as Lennon mustered up the courage to reveal his secret.

"Okay, I've got your word on this, Phil. Here goes—I haven't written even one song since I've been back in L.A., and that's over six months now."

"Yeah?" Spector said eagerly. "And?"

"And that's it," Lennon said. "I've tried every day, but nothing's coming."

"That's what's bugging you?" Spector was incredulous. Also more than a little disappointed. "Shit, John, that's *nothing*. With all this hush-hush business, I thought you had a real *problem.* Jesus!" Spector started laughing. "I thought it was *serious,* for chrissakes. Thought you were *broke* or something. *Queer* even, I don't know. You made it sound so horrible."

Lennon didn't appreciate Spector's casual disregard. "To me, it *is* horrible. It's a bloody nightmare. I'm an artist. I can't create. If this keeps up, I might as well *be* broke. Creating's where I make my money."

"John! Forget it. You've still got it. You're going through a cold period, that's all. It doesn't mean anything. Happens to everybody in this business. Happened to *me* for chrissakes! If you couldn't *write,* you couldn't have *written,* and you've written more monsters than I can even remember. Look, take my advice and *do an oldies album*

CREEM

Lennon's incident at the Troubadour nightclub received widespread national coverage. Here's a sample from Creem Magazine, *the well-known rock journal published in Detroit.*

THE BEAT GOES ON

Another Day In The Life

By now some of you may have heard "rumors" to the effect that John Lennon made an entrance at the Troubadour club in Hollywood a short while ago adorned with a Kotex on his forehead. Well the way things turned out, that was no rumor but the truth. And for those interested in further details here's the entire story in its unexpurgated version (as told by a close confidante of the ex-Beatle).

The story goes that John

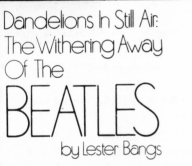

Dandelions In Still Air: The Withering Away Of The BEATLES
by Lester Bangs

of brownstones right next to each other. . ."

But that's hearsay. What isn't is that John has been staying drunk a lot, making a public spectacle of himself with such shamelss elan that Lou Reed is gonna have to hustle his ass or lose the crown: kotexes on the forehead, standing on tables in nightclubs screaming "I'm John Lennon! I'm John Lennon!," disrupting the stage acts of his peers in a manner more befitting Iggy Pop or perhaps the famous Lenny Bruce - Pearl Bailey incident in Vegas.

for chrissakes! A rock & roll oldies album! You singing and me producing, that mother'll ship platinum, you'll see yourself back on top of the charts, and *that's* when your songs will start coming."

"You've hit it on the head, Phil. I've lost my confidence."

"Hey—we're all insecure. How do I know I'm not gonna walk outside tomorrow and get run over by a truck? Then what good are all my millions gonna do me?"

"You're really cheering me up."

"Nothing's gonna cheer you up, pal, until you get off your butt and stop mind-fucking this thing. Just be at Gold Star Studios tonight at eight. I'll take care of the musicians, the instruments, everything. You just think of some oldies you want to do."

"Thanks, Phil. By the way, where is Gold Star? I've never heard of it."

Spector was shocked. "You've *never heard of* Gold Star Studios? Are you kidding?"

"No, I'm not kidding," Lennon told him. "What's so special about Gold Star, anyway?"

"*What's so special? What's so special?*" Spector couldn't believe his ears. "Gold Star, John, is where rock & roll history was created! Gold Star is where I cut the Ronettes. Gold Star is where I cut the Crystals. Gold Star is where I cut the Righteous Brothers. Gold Star is where—"

"*Where is Gold Star, Phil?*" Lennon had run out of patience. "We can talk about the old days some other time."

"The corner of Santa Monica and Vine," Spector said.

"Then I'll see you there at eight. Okay?"

"Right," Spector said. "You know, it's funny—it was at 8:00 p.m. on a Thursday just like this when I cut 'You've Lost That Lovin' Feeling' for the Righteous Brothers, and it was at eight on a Thursday when I cut 'Be My Baby' for the Ronettes, and it was the same day and time for the Crystals and 'Da Doo Ron Ron'—"

"*Phil!* Stop living in the past, willya?"

"Oh . . . sorry. Just miss those days, I guess." Spector's voice was full of hurt. Now Lennon felt guilty.

"Phil, I know you haven't been getting the hits lately, but what you've got to realize is that you're just going through a cold period, that's all. It happens to everybody in this business. You've still got it. Don't worry."

"Thanks, John," Spector said, brightening. "I needed to hear that." He hung up.

For a full minute, Lennon sat and stared at the phone receiver he was holding in his right hand. Then he shook his head in amazement and hung up.

The album that came out of those sessions, *Rock & Roll*, was Lennon's best solo effort. Temporarily free of the restrictions and inhibitions placed upon him by the "genius" label he'd earned as a Beatle, Lennon sounded loose and had fun with the vintage classics on *Rock & Roll*. But its release coincided with several other oldies albums from established artists, tarnishing much of the idea's novelty and cutting into sales, as well. For an ex-Beatle—John Lennon particularly—*Rock & Roll* was not considered a big-seller. And Spector's claim that Lennon's creativity would return proved inaccurate. The follow-up album, *Walls & Bridges* (the title supposedly a reference to Lennon's writer's block) was even less successful, both artistically and commercially. And as if things weren't bad enough, the United States was trying to deport him as an undesirable alien. He spent the next two years in court, fighting the deportation and still another legal wrangle over "Come Together," a song on the *Break Up* album which the publishers of Chuck Berry's "You Can't Catch Me" claimed was plagiarized from their song.

In January of 1979, at the lowest ebb of his professional career, John Lennon was quite receptive to Paul McCartney's proposal of a Beatles' reunion.

"I'm all for it," Lennon told McCartney, who called from London. "Let's go back to work. I'm ready. No bullshit this time. It's not worth it. I'll even go for Eastman if you still want him . . ."

"You were the last one," McCartney told him. "George and Ringo agreed this morning."

"Where *is* George?" John asked McCartney. "Ringo I see now and again, he's only a few miles from here. But where'd you find George?"

"Hanging out at Warner Brothers Records in Burbank. Spends all his days there."

"That's right," Lennon said, "he's with Warners now. You're with Capitol, Ringo's with Atlantic, and my contract just expired. I'm the only free agent of the bunch. How can we get together if we're all on different labels?"

"It's a problem, I know, but I don't think it's insurmountable. In fact, it might be easier than we think. People want us to get together again so badly, that nobody—no one person or no one company—would want to be the one that prevented it. It would be disastrous from a public relations standpoint."

The conversation continued for several more minutes, both Lennon and McCartney mapping out strategy, contingencies, and logistics. Considering the subject matter, it was a very sober, businesslike exchange, much like the conversation McCartney had with Harrison and Ringo Starr earlier that day. Lennon was somewhat self-conscious about it all.

"It's funny," he said to McCartney. "It's like we're a couple of corporation presidents discussing a merger, instead of two musicians about to play again."

"That's exactly what I was thinking," McCartney revealed, "this morning after I spoke to George and Ringo. I put it down to the inevitability of it all. I mean, deep down, none of this is a surprise, is it? Did you ever really believe—I mean *really*—that this day wouldn't come, that we wouldn't get back together ultimately?"

Lennon laughed. It was the first moment of levity in the entire conversation. He could hear McCartney's familiar laugh on the other end.

"You know," he told McCartney, "fuck all this business shit. It's going to be good writing with you again."

McCartney returned the unexpected compliment, set a meeting at Ringo's house the following Thursday in Los Angeles, and hung up.

24

All Together Now

February 5, 1979 was one of those Southern California days the natives seldom brag about—doing so would be asking for even more of the overpopulation that shares with smog the distinction of being the area's only drawbacks. It was sunny, cloudless, and 75° at two in the afternoon when John Lennon's Rolls Royce turned in to Ringo Starr's driveway at the top of Sunset Plaza Road. The side gate to the relatively small yard was open and Lennon was delighted to see the other three—and *only* the other three, no wives or girlfriends—in the yard. Ringo and McCartney were hunched over the billiards table, unaware of Lennon's presence. George Harrison—immaculately dressed in a cream-white suit—spotted Lennon immediately from the lounge chair by the swimming pool. They smiled at each other, then Lennon crossed himself dramatically with his right hand just to demonstrate that his own level of respect for Harrison's religious beliefs remained unchanged. He crept up to the billiards table, his index finger perpendicular to his lips, a signal to George (and to Ringo, who had spotted him by now) to remain silent. He wanted to surprise McCartney, whose back was still toward him as he approached. When he was only an arms-length away, he suddenly began singing—in his best imitation Paul McCartney voice—a slight variation on "Band on the Run":

"Band on the rag, we're the band on the rag . . ."

McCartney, who had been lining up a shot, froze in

horror, then—in a moment that even George and Ringo found touching—threw his arms around Lennon.

"*On the rag?*" McCartney said moments later, mocking Lennon's parody of his song. "Oh, that's right. I almost forgot. You're the Kotex king of Southern California, aren't you?"

Lennon laughed loudly, then to the others, "Please—no Kotex jokes," without realizing his display of sensitivity was an invitation for more.

"Oh, is it *that* time of the month, John?" George asked. "How were we supposed to know?"

"What happened to *him?*" Lennon asked McCartney, pointing to Harrison. "He used to be so pleasant, so nice to be around. Put him in a corner and he'd meditate all day. Now look at him! With that white suit, he could be the leader of Pimps for Jesus!"

Harrison's laughter could be heard over the others. Ringo pushed a button on the underside of the pool table and a midget appeared with beer, tea, and a bowl containing a variety of mixed nuts and several fat joints.

"Where'd you get the midget?" Lennon asked Ringo.

"Is he a midget?" Ringo deadpanned. "Funny. I never noticed."

George took the straight line. "How would *you* notice? You have to stand on a chair to play billiards."

"John's right about you, George," Ringo said. "You're not the same sweet religious fanatic you once were."

"Pimps for Jesus," Lennon said, popping open a can of Coors.

"Say, George, get me a girl for tonight, then, will you?" Ringo added. "Something, say, about five-feet-two, blonde hair, blue eyes, big tits, nice legs, and familiar with both the Old and New Testament."

"I'll have one of those myself," McCartney said through a mouthful of tuna salad.

"I'll see what I can do," Harrison promised. "And if I have one who's menstruating, I'll save her for you, John."

"I've got nothing against biblical pussy," Lennon said, disregarding Harrison's jibe, "but I do seem to remember something about the Beatles getting back together—"

"I wish they would," McCartney said, mocking the words they'd all heard a million times over the past nine years. "You know, they're all quite talented in their own right, but there was a . . . what's the word I'm looking for, John?"

"I believe the word is 'magic,' isn't it?"

"Right. There was a *magic* that only occurred when they were together, which they haven't been able to duplicate since."

They laughed, but they all knew it was true. There *was* a magic.

"So how do you want to go about it?" Lennon asked. But before any of the others could reply, he had his own answer. "I'm for putting safety pins in our ears like those Punk Rockers"

"With Kotex coming out of our noses!" McCartney added.

"That's the idea," Lennon said weakly, hoping the Kotex bit would go away if he didn't react to it. "Actually, it really doesn't matter what we do," Lennon continued, "so long as we always observe one rule."

"What's that?" Ringo asked.

"Never let George sing," John replied.

"I think he's got a real future in the men's clothing business, myself," McCartney said, opening Harrison's jacket to examine the lining.

Harrison finally defended himself. "What is this? *Pick on George Day?*"

Lennon looked at Ringo. *"Is it?"* he asked wide-eyed and mock-seriously.

"Of course not," Ringo said. "It never falls on a Thursday."

"Well, *whenever* it arrives," Harrison said, "you've all covered yourselves admirably. You'll notice, however, that

I've refrained from being vicious. You haven't heard *me* say one word about our rhythm guitarist's Ipana romance with TV's most lovable twosome, nor have I uttered so much as a syllable about our bass player's pilgrimage through deepest Africa in search of a recording studio that would accept him, nor have I commented on our drummer's pronounced absence from both our car radios and the world in general these past eighteen months."

"That's right, George," Paul said. "And don't think it wasn't appreciated."

"Because it wasn't," John added, laughing.

It went on like this all day long. Every time one of them would attempt to bring up the matter of business, it ended up in some form of hilarity. In a sense, this was the real Beatles' *Reunion,* not the publicly craved-for *Beatles'* Reunion. This was a reunion between four old friends who'd shared the most tumultuous, creative, exhilarating, terrifying, and ultimately gratifying experience of anyone from their generation. Nobody wanted to bring up business, because it was business that drove them apart. Right now it felt too good to bask in that peculiar radiation that everyone experiences at a reunion of this sort. For the Beatles, this experience was heightened a hundredfold. Only those who have risen to the level where they are surrounded daily by no one but those who are either afraid of them or in awe of them can know the terrible loneliness and dehumanization of such a life. Friendship and camaraderie become just faint childhood memories. How could a Beatle be certain of *anyone* who claimed to be a friend, knowing fully well that to grant a Beatle's friendship was to grant a profitable commodity to its recipient—economically, socially, and every other way. It's not surprising they preferred the friendly abuse they were dishing out to each other to the phony, illegitimate praise they'd heard from everyone else in their individual circles for the preceding nine years. Easy to understand, too, their postponing the topic of business that had brought such a terrible and unforeseen loneliness the last time it came up nine years earlier.

Two monstrous pizzas arrived at 8:00, the pizzas being the informal symbol to begin the long-avoided business discussion. The four were seated in Ringo's wood-sculpted dining room, waiting for the midget butler to complete the job of slicing two pizzas, either of which outsized him considerably.

"Let's see, now," McCartney said playfully, "where'd we leave off nine years ago? I believe it was the matter of a manager, correct?"

The other three were devouring pizza, so McCartney continued. "Lee Eastman is still willing and available, but I'll go along with any vote this time."

"Okay by me," Lennon said. Both George and Ringo nodded affirmatively, paying more attention to the pizza than to this particular issue, the raising of which was only a formality on McCartney's part. Lennon had already sold Eastman to the others during the week between Mc-Cartney's phone call and his arrival.

"Now," McCartney continued, "assuming Eastman can extricate us from our present contracts, and he thinks he can if we agree to fulfill our solo commitments to the various labels, then the Beatles as a recording group will go on the bidding block. We'll be free to take the best offer we get, and I imagine it'll be a record-breaking figure, more than Elton John and Stevie Wonder got in their deals *combined*.

"I propose, as soon as possible, that we begin work on the album. There's no reason why we can't be working on it while waiting for the best offer to come in. If everything goes well, we could have the album out by the beginning of the summer, then do a tour, say, in August."

Ringo looked up from his pizza at the mention of the tour. "I didn't know we were going back on the road."

"We have to," Lennon said. "If we're a group, we have to perform. That's how we fell apart before."

Ringo shivered. "My memory of our tours is of one long nightmare."

"Out of shape, Ringo?" George chided him.

"I'm in better shape than I ever was, but that's because I've had thirteen years to recover from our *last* tour."

"What's Jimmy Nicol doing these days?" Lennon asked nobody in particular.

"I hear Pete Best might be available," McCartney announced.

Ringo waved his white napkin over the table in a gesture of surrender.

"Have you two got any tunes?" Harrison asked John and Paul.

"Fresh out," Lennon answered. "What about you, Paul?"

"Same here, but I'm not worried. The old Lennon-McCartney team was never songless for long, were we?"

"Well, I'm dry myself at the moment," Harrison confessed, "but I should have a couple of things ready by the time we record."

"Isn't anybody going to ask *me?*" Ringo asked with a hurt voice.

"Okay, Ringo," George said with great resignation. He knew what was coming. "Do *you* have any songs ready for the new album?"

"Me? Since when am *I* supposed to write songs? I'm just the drummer in this group."

The midget brought more Coors to the table. Ringo held him there while he inquired if the others wanted anything else. "More pizza, Paul? George? John? Kotex for you, perhaps?"

John laughed, then pushed the slice of pizza he was holding into Ringo's face. Thirty minutes of hysteria ensued, then it was back to business.

"What about the press?" George asked Paul. As in the old days, McCartney seemed to have all the answers.

"We can't wait too long. It's a miracle we could get this far without a telephoto lens sticking through the window. I suggest a press conference."

"Then let's do it right away," Harrison said, "and get it over with."

"I'd love to," McCartney told him, "but I still haven't broken the news to the guys in Wings. I wanted to make sure everything was okay between us before I officially disbanded the group. It'd be pretty cruel if they found out from a press conference. It really should come from me personally."

"I don't think we can keep the lid on this until you go back to London and then return here," Harrison said.

"Maybe you can tell them by phone," Lennon suggested.

McCartney considered this for a minute. "I don't like it, but I guess I'll have to, because George is right. It's going to come out anyway, so it's best if we control it ourselves. Since I'm the only one of us that doesn't belong in L.A., why don't I have Capitol schedule a press conference for me on Monday morning? I'll tell them it's for a special Wings announcement. I'll ask them to keep it quiet, which guarantees it'll be all over town by this weekend."

"I've always found the best way to get a message circulated was to give it to Capitol and tell them to keep it a secret," Lennon agreed.

McCartney continued the scenario: "Then Monday morning, I'll show up first and make some bogus announcement about a personnel change in Wings or something, and once the conference is underway, you three show up and we'll drop the bomb for real."

"Pretty dramatic, wouldn't you say?" Ringo asked.

"I'm all for it," Lennon said. "The press has been

fucking with us all these years, let's fuck with them for a change."

"I like your attitude, John," Ringo said.

"Thank you, Ringo. I like your wife."

"Did you say you'd *like* my wife?"

"No I didn't, but now that you mention it—"

"In that case," Ringo said, "talk to George. He handles all her business affairs."

25

I Want to Tell You

Paul McCartney sat behind a battery of microphones in the Platinum Room of the Capitol Tower. Before him were more than a hundred representatives from both the local and the international press. Photographers circled around him like bees hovering around a hive. The president of Capitol Records was concluding an introductory speech, in which he managed to get in a plug for every artist on the Capitol roster *and* a new Sunset Strip restaurant he'd just invested in. He introduced McCartney as "the musical genius of his generation, a man whose lyrics have enlightened and changed the world, and a man who has kept us in the black despite having both Helen Reddy and Glen Campbell on our label."

McCartney waited until the applause died down, then began his prepared statement:

"We've tried to keep it secret, but many of you have already heard that there is to be a change in the status of Wings. I'm here to announce that Wings is losing a member. That member is *me*. As of this morning, I've joined another group."

McCartney paused. The room was completely silent.

"I'd like you to meet the members of my new group," he continued. "Will you come out here, guys?"

Lennon, Harrison, and Ringo entered amidst gasps and screams of recognition. They stood together behind McCartney and were assaulted for the next three minutes by a barrage of flashbulbs. When the noise finally died down, McCartney continued:

"As you no doubt have guessed, the four of us are back together. I'd like to take this opportunity to say that I'm both delighted and excited to be working with my three friends again ... At this time, we'll answer any questions you may have."

"What made you decide to get back together?"

"Our fans did," McCartney said. "They made us what we are today. We owe it to them."

"Will you be performing live?"

"Yes," McCartney said, "we are currently investigating several options, one of which would be a major tour of America late this summer."

"What are your recording plans?"

"We're going right to work on a new album, and we hope to have it in the stores early this summer in advance of the proposed tour. Next?"

By this time, makeshift microphones hauled in from the Capitol recording studio had been placed in front of John, George, and Ringo.

"What label will the new album be on?" asked a reporter from *Billboard* magazine, "and how did you overcome the problem of recording together, when you are all under contract to different companies?"

Lennon took the question.

"Actually, we haven't overcome the problem," he informed the roomful of people, which by now was a madhouse with writers running in and out to phone the news to their offices. "I personally am a free agent at this time, but Ringo is with Atlantic Records, George with Warners, and Paul here at Capitol. It is our belief however, that none of these companies would let their petty, self-serving concerns stand in the way of our re-formation—"

The press stopped Lennon with cheers of solidarity.

"I just can't believe," he continued when the noise subsided, "that the record business would prevent the reunion of the band that statistics prove helped make it into the leading entertainment medium of all—"

Another outburst from the press corps.

"As a matter of fact," Lennon said, about to put into action a piece of strategy which he and McCartney had planned the preceding day, "the president of Paul's label is in the room with us right now. Perhaps we can get his approval while you're all gathered here."

All eyes in the room went directly to Capitol Records president Shep Gold. The president knew that a decision of this magnitude—freeing the biggest moneymaker on his label to entertain multimillion-dollar offers from his competitors—should not be made without at least consulting Capitol's stockholders. But Gold had an uneasy feeling that he wouldn't get out of the room alive if he didn't grant McCartney permission. His perspiration-drenched face smiled as he held up his right hand and gave an "OK" sign to the audience, who responded with a standing ovation. At the podium Lennon and McCartney smiled at each other. Their plan had worked perfectly. McCartney's contract was the only one they had really worried about, expecting little difficulty with either Ringo's or George's, since neither was selling particularly well for their respective record companies.

More questions followed. *Were they going to continue their solo careers?* Yes, when time permitted, but the first consideration was the Beatles. *Why had they now agreed to Lee Eastman as their manager when the dispute over him had led to the original breakup?* Because it facilitated the re-formation, and any business matters were secondary. Getting the Beatles back together was the important thing.

After an hour, the questions grew increasingly trivial, and Capitol president Shep Gold strode to the podium.

"Thank you all very much for coming," he said. "I'm

Los Angeles Times—Tuesday, February 13, 1979.

sure you won't be going away disappointed from this press conference. In closing, I'd like to say this: although the Beatles were quite successful in their various solo careers, when they're together there's a certain uh, uh excuse me, I'm trying to think of the right word—"

"Magic," Lennon said into his microphone.

"Yes, magic . . . there's a certain magic that occurs only when they're together. When you leave here to write your articles today, you might mention that Capitol has many, many Beatle albums in our catalog which demonstrate this magic like nothing else . . ."

He began reading a four-page list of available Beatle products on Capitol, but by the time he'd finished the first page, the room was empty.

26

It Don't Come Easy

"I knew it would be crazy," John Lennon said the morning after the press conference as he welcomed Paul McCartney into his Benedict Canyon mansion, "but I never expected this much response."

"I did," McCartney said, seating himself at the table in the corner of Lennon's spacious kitchen. "I was on the road a whole summer with Wings in '76. Really *out there*, you know," his finger was pointing toward the kitchen window, "and you just wouldn't believe the Beatle fever I saw. Since Elvis died we're all that's left. I tell you it's like we're gods or something—"

"Would you say we're bigger than Jesus Christ?" Lennon joked.

"You might have been right about that," McCartney said, as he gave his breakfast order to the maid, one of three employed full-time by Lennon.

"Jesus," Lennon sighed. "Front page headline in the *Los Angeles Times* this morning, all over the news, the whole record business took the day off, declaring it a holiday—"

"I hear they broke into TV programs yesterday to give the news," McCartney said.

"I heard. Yoko told me they even interrupted 'Gilligan's Island.'"

"Don't tell me you finally got her to watch 'Gilligan's Island'!"

"Sure did. Otherwise we'd still be separated. It was the

key part of our reconciliation. After all, it's what broke us up in the first place."

"Just so long as you don't make *me* watch it," McCartney told him.

"With all due respect, Paul, I don't think you've got the mental capacity required to transcend the surface level of 'Gilligan's Island' in order to get to the allegorical levels of the show where the *real* story is."

McCartney let the matter drop, not knowing if Lennon was serious and afraid to find out that he might be.

"Ready to write some songs?" he asked Lennon as they were finishing off breakfast.

"I don't know. I don't feel particularly inspired this morning."

"I never knew you to be inspired in the mornings," McCartney reassured him. "You're a night person."

"I know. But I don't get particularly inspired at night lately either."

"When *do* you get inspired? Afternoons?"

"I don't know. I haven't been inspired for such a long time, I can't remember what time of day it was."

"Well, none of that matters now," McCartney said. "I'm here, and when you and me get together—"

"It's magic, right?"

"What's with this fascination with *white?*" McCartney asked from behind a white piano in Lennon's music room. The entire room—walls, curtains, furniture, carpeting, even the artwork—was all the same shade of white.

"Yoko's idea," Lennon answered through a mouthful of white pistachio nuts. "She figured it'd help me create if my senses weren't assaulted with color. Hasn't, though." He sank into the plush sofa until he almost disappeared from McCartney's view. "I kind of like it anyway," his muffled voice emerged from its upholstered depths. "Certainly posh and elegant."

McCartney began playing random chords on the

piano. "Stop me if you hear something," he instructed Lennon.

"Hold it there," Lennon said a few minutes later. "Play that bit again."

"Here, let me find it. There. This it?" McCartney played the melody again and again.

"Yeah!" Lennon jumped up and grabbed a Gibson acoustic guitar, and began strumming the chords. He started singing:

"There are places I remember all my life, but some have changed . . ."

McCartney took over:

"Some forever, not for better, some have gone and some remain . . ."

McCartney stopped suddenly.

"What'd you stop for?" Lennon asked. "That's a great song."

"I know. It was a great song fifteen years ago, too, when we first wrote it."

"We don't seem to be getting anywhere," McCartney said two hours later. By now, they were both on the sofa, each holding guitars that might as well have been baseball bats for all they were getting out of them.

"I'm quite familiar with the feeling," Lennon said, buzzing the maid for tea. She entered and quietly placed the silver tray onto the white marble coffee table. Lennon was immersed in thought. McCartney was aimlessly strumming chords.

"What's wrong with us, Paul?" Lennon asked.

"What do you mean?"

"I used to have so many bloody songs running through my head, it was all I could do just to write them all down. And when we'd write together, it was so nonstop we used to go crazy."

"I was thinking the same thing myself," McCartney confessed. "Remember back in Hamburg, those afternoons in that stinking room we all shared in the Star Club? One toilet for four of us and it was always backing up—"

"Could have used Brian back then."

"It was so *easy* in those days. I can remember us writing 'Please Please Me,' 'I Saw Her Standing There,' 'From Me to You,' and 'There's a Place' all in one summer afternoon when that little room stunk so bad you could barely breathe."

"I remember that day!" Lennon said excitedly. "Sure. Just like it was yesterday, I can remember it. We were thinking of packing it all in, but we didn't have the money to get back to Liverpool—"

"Right. And we resolved to really get serious about our songwriting, so even if the group never took off, you and me could make a living without having to get regular jobs."

"And we swore we'd never again suffer the indignity of living like pigs in shit."

"Yeah," McCartney recalled. "I remember when we finished 'There's a Place,' you brought all the waitresses up to the room to hear it, and you were bragging about how it was going to be number one in a year and we'd never have to take shit from Klaus [Reepervon, owner of the Star Club] again."

"Right. But they didn't believe us. Nobody believed us," Lennon said, the old rage coming back. "We showed them, though. We showed all those bastards."

Lennon sunk back into the couch. In only a moment his face, so animated seconds earlier, had taken on the vacant look that McCartney recognized as depression.

"What's wrong, John?"

"Nothing. Nothing important."

"Something's bothering you. What is it?"

"I hate talking about the old days, that's all."

"Why?"

"Because what I remember most is never a specific *thing*, it's always a *feeling* I remember."

"Yes?"

"It's a feeling I never get anymore," Lennon explained. "It's that feeling of satisfaction from knowing that someday you were just going to dump on everyone who'd been dumping on you. You know what I mean?"

"Yes."

"I used to dream—well, *you* must have had the same dream, so you probably felt the same way—of making it, really making it."

"Sure. That great day when we could tell the whole world to fuck off."

"Right. And that dream used to *fuel* me. I had so much goddamn energy in those days, it amazes me now. I used to get more ideas on a twenty-minute walk to the grocery store than I do now sitting around for a month in this bloody room." Lennon kicked the silver tray off the coffee table, splattering tea all over the white carpeting.

"Nobody took your dream away from you, John," McCartney said, bending over to pick up the serving tray. "The only thing that happened to your dream was that it came true."

"But you don't understand. I always had that dream, ever since I was old enough to realize there was something better than what I had as a kid. That dream had always been with me. It was like my partner, my inspiration. Talk about inspiration! That dream was a lot more inspiration than any bird's ever been, before or since.

"So here I am," Lennon continued, "walking through life, me and my dream—"

"And suddenly the dream became a reality, and was thereby taken away from you," McCartney finished.

"You know exactly what I'm saying, don't you?" Lennon realized. "We've lived the same life." A wave of sentimentality crept over him. He never remembered feeling as close to McCartney as he did at that moment.

"So *this* is our dream," Lennon continued, sweeping his arm around the room. "Our dream come true. And now, you and I sit here on this plush sofa in this plush room, drinking tea served upon a silver platter, and we sit here for three fucking hours without even an *idea* for a song. It's all gone. It's all over. That creative rush. We'll never see it again. I mean, what was it all for? Banging our heads against a wall for years, finally getting somewhere, finally realizing our dream, and then this!"

"I know," McCartney said. "I know. But what do you do? I mean, you can't kill yourself."

"It's entered my mind."

"Come off it, John. It isn't that bad. You just have to get used to the idea. You have to adjust to it. I did it and you can do it, too."

"How do you mean, 'adjust'?"

"You just use the ideas you have, that's all. Whatever ideas you get, you just use them. Your problem is that you're waiting for the kind of wonderful brilliant ideas you used to get in the old days when we were trying to make it. Well, forget it. You're right about that much. Those ideas *are* gone. They disappeared the same time our dream did. But you're still a creative person, just like I am. We *need* to create. And if the stuff we're creating is inferior to what we created ten or fifteen years ago, so what? We've already got all the money and all the recognition we'll ever need."

"With me, it's more like a *hunger* to create. It's like I'm starving."

"Exactly!" McCartney exclaimed. "That's exactly what I'm talking about. Look at it that way. Just because you can't eat the same quality food you ate ten years ago, that doesn't mean you should starve yourself, does it? You eat whatever you can, and enjoy it as much as you can. Maybe it doesn't taste as good as it did a long time ago, but it keeps you alive. It keeps you sane."

"So *that* explains your songs these past few years, doesn't it?" Lennon asked.

"Of course. You think I'd have been writing 'Silly Love

Songs' if I had the same juice flowing through me that I did in Liverpool? No way."

"So you *knew* it was inferior, but you went ahead with it anyway."

"Right. It satisfied my hunger, my creative instinct. I enjoyed making that music, even though it may have been 'inferior' to what I once did. But how about *your* music?" McCartney said accusingly. "You must have realized the tunes you were writing were vastly inferior to your Beatles work—"

"I never really was positive, so I convinced myself they were equally as good or better even. It was the only way I could record them. I *still* don't really know if they were better or not."

"Then let me tell you. They weren't. But now that you know, do you think you'd have been better off not working at all?"

Lennon didn't answer. Too many things were running through his mind.

"Accept it, John. You're never going to have the ideas you once had, and neither am I. But if you worry about surpassing your old songs, all you'll do is block out any new ones. Never mind what people expect from us. We know what *our* needs are, and *that's* who we'll write for— ourselves."

"Hey!" Lennon said enthusiastically. "I just got an idea for a song about 'Gilligan's Island.' " He started working out a chord change.

"Now you're talking!" McCartney said, and seated himself behind the piano.

27

Get Back

The reunion album, *Get Back*, was to be recorded during the months of April and May in the studio at Phil Spector's Beverly Hills estate. McCartney was opposed to having Spector produce the album, preferring George Martin, producer of all earlier Beatles albums (with the exception of *Break Up*). But Lennon and Spector had grown very close in the years following the Beatles' demise and Lennon said he wouldn't feel comfortable with anyone but Spector.

"Besides," he said to McCartney, "have you heard that crap George Martin's been doing with America? Is that what you want for us?"

"Well, we're not America. We're bigger than America."

"We're bigger than Jesus, too, but that doesn't mean we shouldn't use the best producer in the business."

George Harrison arrived a moment later.

"Tell George how big we are, John," McCartney said.

"I'd rather not, if you don't mind."

"What's all this about?" Harrison asked.

"Oh, John says we're bigger than—"

"*America!*" Lennon cut in.

"Kind of an overstatement, I would think," Harrison reflected. "Awfully big country. I think we might be bigger than Pittsburgh, though."

While the Beatles were busy in the recording studio, Lee Eastman's work was cut out for him. Both a recording deal *and* a tour had to be arranged.

Eastman met with representatives from every major label, taking their bids into consideration and telling them they'd hear from him. The bids were so astronomically high that Eastman felt it wouldn't be in the group's interest to commit to any one company for more than one album, and first rights to the follow-up. After that the whole lucrative bidding process could begin again.

The top two offers came from CBS (Columbia, Epic, and their family of labels) and Atlantic Records. Each was offering an equal amount of money ("more than the Gross National Product of many countries," claimed *Billboard* magazine) in both advances and royalties. The decision would be made on the basis of fringe benefits. At a break in the *Get Back* sessions, Eastman asked the group if there was anything they'd like in the way of benefits tacked on to their recording contract.

"I'd like a plumber on call at my house twenty-four hours," Lennon said. "You're a good manager, Lee, but you're terrible when it comes to a leaky faucet."

Eastman noted this and asked for more.

"I'd like it stipulated," Ringo said, "that there be a fully equipped billiards table in my suite at every stop on the tour."

"That would have to be handled by the individual promoters, wouldn't it, Lee?" McCartney asked.

"Ordinarily, yes," Eastman answered. "But this is a special situation. We can get the labels to give us *anything*. You'll have it, Ringo. Now, what else?"

"I'd like to see the label sign up the guys in Wings as solo artists. They deserve a good recording deal," McCartney said.

"Done," Eastman replied. "George?"

"I''ve got an unusual request," Harrison said. "I don't know if they can do it."

"Trust me," Eastman said with great assurance. "They can do anything, and they *will* do anything to get the Beatles. Now what is it?"

"I want them to buy the master tapes of all my solo

albums except the first one, and destroy them. And I also want them to buy every single copy of those albums from every record store in the world, and destroy those, too. Those records are detrimental to my reputation."

"That *is* a big request, George, but I'm sure they can handle it. I'll have to personally oversee the project, to ensure that it's done with discretion. Now, does that cover it?"

"Think they could get Sonny Bono bumped off?" Lennon asked.

"I'm sure they could," Eastman replied, laughing, "and if they thought that's what it took to get the Beatles, I'm sure they *would*. But if it came out that we were behind such a conspiracy, it might hurt our image somewhat."

Eastman left hurriedly and the group returned to the studio. An hour later, they heard from him again.

"We're with CBS," he told McCartney via telephone. "Columbia Records. They've agreed to everything. Even *offered* to knock off Sonny Bono—I didn't bring it up—but I think that's because he's still under contract to their TV division for $250,000 a year, even though 'The Sonny & Cher Show' was canceled three years ago."

Lennon and McCartney had collaborated on six songs—"Gilligan's Island," "Yoko's Going Broke-o," "Son of Pizza Man," "Hold On To Your Dream," "Please Freeze Me," and "Maybe I'm Amazed, Maybe I'm Not (It's None of Your Business)." George Harrison made a valiant attempt at commerciality with his two tunes, "Disco Jesus" and "Bring the Captain In to Kneel (Before the Altar)."

Spector informed the group they'd need another song to fill out the album, as their eight originals combined clocked in at only twenty-nine minutes.

John and Paul looked at each other and shook their heads, as if to say "no way" when they heard the news.

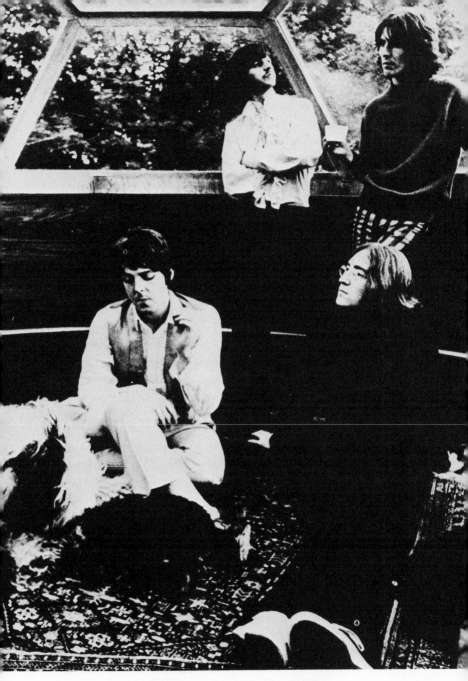

**Listening to playback of *Get Back*, April 1979,
reunited Beatles see eye-to-eye on its merit.**

Their six songs had squeezed them dry and they knew it.

"Don't look at me," Harrison said.

"Come on, George," John said, "You're the one who always used to complain about not getting your songs recorded."

"That was before I put them all on my first album," he replied.

"Enough. Enough," Phil Spector said, entering the studio from the control booth. "We can either stand here and *worry* about this or we can solve the problem. This exact situation occurred when I had Philles Records. We were two songs short on the Righteous Brothers' *You've Lost That Lovin' Feelin'* album—"

"Phil!" McCartney cut in. "Please! No more memories of the good old days. I hear one more word about your legendary old Philles label, and I'm walking out."

Lennon was aghast at McCartney's behavior. He ran over to him, grabbed his right arm, and began dragging the protesting McCartney across the room toward Spector, shouting, "You're gonna apologize!" over and over into McCartney's ear. Finally McCartney shook himself loose.

"No! I'm *not* apologizing. I said it and I meant it! If he wants to produce our album, fine. I'll go along with whatever the majority wants. But if he doesn't cut it out with that 'good old days' crap, I'm gonna get sick. I've learned enough about Philles Records these last two months to write a book. And I would, too, except it's *boring*. Boring, boring, boring!"

Although McCartney's distaste for Spector was not a secret, none of them suspected it ran so deep.

"Paul," John said, "Phil is a genius. And genius is pain. I know that from experience. Phil is constantly in pain—"

"He's gonna be in a lot more pain if he keeps up that 'good old days' crap," McCartney threatened.

Through all of this, Spector sat serenely behind Ringo's drum kit. When things quieted down, he went back into action.

"All right. All right. Are we all done with this petty

animosity, kiddies? What we need, since none of you are prepared to write another song, is someone else's material. Any suggestions?"

At this point, an argument *really* started. Everyone had his own choice for the song which would complete *Get Back*.

"I suggest 'This Could Be the Start of Something Big,' " Ringo said.

"What's *that*?" Lennon asked.

"Steve Allen's theme song," Ringo answered. "Been humming it for weeks. Can't get it out of my head."

"That's a good place for it. Why don't you just keep it there?" McCartney advised.

"Let's do an oldie," Harrison suggested.

"Sure, George," Lennon said snidely. "You know the chords to 'He's So Fine' by any chance?"

"I'd tell him to go to hell," Harrison said to Spector, ignoring Lennon, "but he's going anyway."

"How about 'Young Americans,' the old Bowie tune?" McCartney suggested. "It would tie in perfectly with the American tour."

"Nah, everyone's been doing Bowie songs since the plane crash," Lennon said. "It'd look like we were trying to cash in on his death."

"There's always 'Be My Baby,' " Spector said nervously. McCartney shot him a look so cold that the producer had to leave the room to get a sweater.

"I've got it!" Lennon said. "Heard it on the radio on the way over here today. A forgotten classic."

"Are we supposed to *guess* the title?" Harrison asked.

"You never would in a million years," Lennon continued. "Remember the old David Crosby tune, 'Almost Cut My Hair'?"

"*That* piece of shit?" Harrison said. "What about it?"

"How can you call it a piece of shit?" Lennon demanded. "It's got everything 'Gilligan's Island' has, except in song form."

"He asks me a question," George said to Ringo, "and

then he goes ahead and answers it himself. Is this any way to communicate?"

Through a combination of Lennon's persistence and the recording fatigue they all felt, Lennon managed to get his way on "Almost Cut My Hair." They finished it in three hours, and it completed the album, except for the final mix, which Lennon and Spector were handling.

After the others had departed, Spector asked Lennon about McCartney.

"Why doesn't he like me? I don't understand it. I'm such a mellow guy. Back in the old days, I was a terror, though. I'd fire people if they bumped into me accidentally. One time, after we'd finished 'He's a Rebel,' this promotion man from Jewel Records came into the studio and wanted me to sign up his group, two black guys and a white girl. He said his group was so hot they could eat the Ronettes for breakfast. I reached back, grabbed a reel of one-inch tape, and wrapped it around his throat—"

"*Phil!* One more word about the bloody 'old days' and I give these tapes to George Martin!"

"Okay! Okay! Sorry ... Now, tell me the truth—" Spector leaned toward Lennon to ensure privacy for his reply. "Why doesn't Paul like me?"

"*I don't know, Phil!*" Lennon exploded. "Would you like to hear why *I* don't like you?"

"Shit, John. You love me and you know it. We're both geniuses. We've both lived with the same pain."

"What?" Lennon asked, surprised. "You didn't tell me Yoko moved in with you."

28

Not a Second Time

Ronald Number, the National Vice President of Promotion for Columbia Records, was frantic. He arrived at the label's New York headquarters at 10 A.M. after an all-night flight from Los Angeles.

"What happened to *you?*" the receptionist at Columbia asked the disheveled, unshaven figure clutching a reel of tape in one hand, holding onto the reception desk with the other.

"Never mind that, honey. Just tell Soption to cancel whatever he's got this morning to fit me in. This can't wait." He spotted a chair and collapsed into it. She rang Lee Soption, Columbia Records President.

"Mr. Soption says he's supposed to present a gold record to Chicago for *Chicago 27* in ten minutes," the receptionist told Number. "He wants to know if you can wait until this afternoon."

"This afternoon?" Number screamed. "We've already waited too long!" He ran over to the switchboard and grabbed the phone from the receptionist.

"Lee? This is Ron. I've got to talk to you. This can't wait. *What?* Fuck Chicago! This is *big* . . . I don't care, make them wait. Tell them to beat off into their horns for an hour, what do I care? I'm telling you this is *hot*. What? Fine. Okay, be right up." He handed the phone back to the receptionist, suggesting she quickly change into some old clothes.

"Why? What's wrong with what I'm wearing?"

"Darling," Number said confidentially, "there's gonna be so much shit flying around this building before the day's over, you'll be lucky to even *recognize* that dress of yours by five o'clock."

The head of National Promotion is probably the second-most important executive in the structure of a record company, right behind the president (*far* behind the president in salary, however). He's in charge of getting airplay for his company's product, and in the record business, airplay equals dollars. Ron Number was one of the best, and Columbia president Lee Soption knew it. Number came up through the ranks, starting in the mailroom, and quickly landing a local promotion job at Columbia by ingeniously making everyone believe the job was already his while he was still working in the mailroom. Instead of mailing out records, he'd take them to local radio stations and promote them as though it was his job. Soon he had the radio stations believing he was a promotion man, and there was little that Columbia could do except make it official. Nine months later, he was promoted to a regional post with the company, covering the entire Northeast. After a tremendously successful two-year run as regional promotion director, Capitol offered him the national position with their company. To keep him, Soption fired *his* national man and gave Number the job.

"This had better be important," Soption said as Number walked into the president's twenty-fourth-floor office. "I've got Chicago waiting on the fourteenth floor, and you know how sensitive they are."

"Oh, fuck them. They're washed up anyway."

"How can you say that? Their albums still go gold."

"People buy them out of habit," Number said, "or else to get the complete set, like those annuals they make every year for encyclopedias."

"I'll be happy to discuss the merits of Chicago with you at a more convenient time. Now, what is so goddamn important that this whole company has to grind to a halt over?"

"I want you to hear a tape, Lee."

"What? A tape? Are you crazy? I've got business to attend to this morning!" (If there was such a thing as a list of *Requests Made of a Record Company President,* Would You Please Listen to This Tape? would be number one with a bullet.)

"You'll understand in a minute, Lee," Number said while he threaded the tape through Soption's Teac machine. When it was set up, he turned toward his boss and said, "Now, I'm gonna skip through this tape, playing part of each song, and when I'm done, I want your honest, gut reaction to it."

Number proceeded to play a minute or two of each song on the tape.

"Your opinion?"

"My opinion, Ron, is despite the fact that I love you like a brother, you'd better have a pretty fucking good reason for disrupting my entire morning to play me that godawful shit. If you want to keep your job, I mean. What is it? Some local group? Your brother-in-law's band? Level with me."

"You don't like it, right?" Number was trying to separate Soption's anger from his opinion.

"It's the worst piece of unadulterated shit I've heard in over twenty years in this business. Am I making myself clear enough?"

"It's also something else, Lee."

"What?"

"It's the new Beatles album."

By the end of May, Eastman had finalized the summer tour, opening up at Dodger Stadium in Los Angeles August 2, with twenty-five shows to follow, concluding at

Shea Stadium August 31. As part of an ingenious market-
ing strategy devised by Eastman, all promoters agreed to
honor only those ticket requests on a special order blank
found in the new Beatles album, due in the stores June 5.
Eastman was also able to convince the eager promoters to
pay the Beatles a previously unheard-of 90 percent of the
gross receipts (in the 50,000-seat baseball stadiums where
the majority of the tour was to be staged, this would
amount to—at $15 a head—a cool $675,000 for the Beatles
for a night's work, or more than $17 million for the
twenty-six-show tour).

"Gentlemen, the matter about to be discussed is of a
top-secret nature," Lee Soption told the twenty-four
various department vice-presidents seated around an enormous table in the company's conference room. "We've got
a problem on our hands, and I need your input if we're
going to solve it.

"As you know, CBS practically went into hock to
acquire both the new Beatles album, and the first-option
rights on the follow-up album. Having the Beatles on
Columbia made sense. The biggest belong with the
biggest, and it was the proudest day of my twenty-year
career in this industry when I signed them to Columbia. I
didn't foresee then—who could have?—the problem we're
faced with now. And what is that problem, you ask? Ron,
roll the tape . . ."

Ron Number clicked the machine into gear and
returned to his seat. The twenty-four vice-presidents were
listening to "Gilligan's Island" from the new Beatles
album:

> Bob Denver, Jim Backus
> Each day they attack us
> With laughter, fun, and truth.

But I'd like to squeeze
Miss Tina Louise
To get us both a-smilin'
We'd make love until three
When on local TV, it's time for
Gilligan's Island.

Then, to "Yoko's Going Broke-o":

They won't sell her art
At the supermart
They claim it is a joke-o

This has to stop,
Quite soon, I fear, for
Yoko's going broke-o.

They don't buy her bags,
Don't buy her blintzes,
Don't buy her milk bottles in the snow-ko

Perhaps they'll change
When they get the news that
Yoko's going broke-o.

During "Yoko's Going Broke-o," Number found himself questioning the usefulness of the meeting.

"What's the point of this meeting anyway?" he asked Soption over the music.

"These are my key people, Ron. These are the best brains in the company. If anybody's likely to have a solution to the problem, it'll be one of them."

Number couldn't believe what he was hearing. How out of touch *was* the old man, anyway?

"Lee, none of these guys is going to say anything useful for *any* of us. All they're gonna do is the same thing they always do: find out what your opinion is and agree with it. There isn't a decent set of balls in this whole room."

"I can't believe that, Ron. These are vice-presidents.

The upper echelon of the entire company. And you're saying they didn't get there through ability, but only by kissing my ass? You're way off, buddy."

Like any good promotion man, Number knew the weaknesses and vulnerabilities of those he was promoting. Soption's was gambling.

"I've got five hundred bucks in my back pocket," Number told his boss, "that says these guys—every one of them—will agree with you if you say this album is the greatest piece of recorded music in history."

"Come on, Ron. I'd be taking your money. This music is so bad, it's embarrassing. Look around the room. They *hate* it, all of them. Artie and Sal over there are giggling, look at them."

"Is it a bet or isn't it?"

"It's a bet."

When "Yoko's Going Broke-o" finished, Number turned off the machine, and Soption returned to his place at the head of the table.

"As you can hear," Soption told his vice-presidents, "the problem with this new Beatles album is that it's so good, so uniformly brilliant, it's going to be almost *impossible* to select just one cut for a single. But that's our problem. I'd like to go around the table now, and find out what each of you think about this new product of ours. Let's start with you, Artie."

"It's great, Lee. I love it."

"Thank you, Artie. How about you, Sal?"

"Dynamite, Lee. Triple platinum for sure."

"Charlie?"

"What can I say? It's a monster!"

Soption could hear Number's muffled laughter.

"Stan, how about you?"

"It's a mother, Lee. Debut number one in *Billboard*. You watch."

"Frank?"

"So beautiful, Lee, I almost started crying. The Beatles

back together, and better than ever. It's just so beautiful."

"Harvey?"

"Tremendous. Absolute killer. I think the single should be the last one we heard, the 'Yoko' one. They'll eat it up out there."

As the comments continued, Soption wrote out a $500 check, signed it, and slid it across the table to Number. A note was attached:

Stick around. This is going to get very interesting.

"You're last, Mel," Soption said. "How'd you like the album?"

"Lee, there comes a time, I mean, wow, like you know when you're in on musical history, and I feel like that time came for me a few minutes ago in this room. Whew! I mean, what can I say?"

"I've got something to say if you don't," Soption said, rising from his chair. "Either all of you are deaf—in which case you have no business working here—or else you're the worst bunch of ass-kissers I've ever had the pleasure of firing."

Soption paused. Confusion set in.

"Did he just fire us?"

"What'd he say?"

"Are we fired?"

"I don't get it."

"Gentlemen, please . . ." Soption waited until he had their attention. "There appears to be a bit of confusion among you regarding the statement I just made. Let me clear that up right now: I just played for all of you a portion of an album that's such an obvious turkey, it shouldn't be released until Thanksgiving. And each and every one of you told me it was great. *I'm not paying you guys to kiss my ass!* That is, as of now, I'm not paying you to kiss my ass. Because *you're all fired!* Does that help to clear things up? Thank you for your service to the company, and make sure you're out of this building by two o'clock this afternoon or I call the cops. Meeting adjourned!"

As the dazed executives began filing out of the meeting room, Soption sat down next to Number.

"Well, what'd you think of that, Ron?"

"Great Lee! Dynamite! Beautiful! I love it! Makes me cry . . ."

"Enough, enough," Soption laughed. "You made your point."

Number got up and walked out of the room, stopping at the door.

"Lee!" he shouted from across the room. "One more thing . . ."

"What?"

"From the bottom of my heart, man, that was a dynamite decision. It was beautiful. A killer! Platinum, that's what it was. I mean, wow! It was like history in the making! What can I say?"

"Try 'good-bye,' and as quickly as possible. And while you're at it, try to think of a way to get radio stations to play our Beatles album more than once."

It was June 3, 1979. Two days before the official release date of *Get Back*. Ron Number was dodging in and out of the Los Angeles traffic on his way to radio station KLOS, the city's leading Progressive Rock FM outlet. As he burst inside the station, he spotted KLOS program director, Thomas "Toke" Madison.

"Toke! I've got it!" Number held up a white album cover.

"You mean the new—"

Number held his finger to his lips. "Right."

Madison quickly ushered him toward the studio.

"This is a test pressing, Toke. The album's not due out for two more days," Number said excitedly as they entered the studio. "Whatever you do, you've got to promise not to say I leaked this copy to you. It's against company policy to give out exclusives."

"Don't worry about a thing," Madison assured him, delighted with the opportunity to have the new Beatles album exclusively on his station for two full days before his competition. He'd have the whole city listening to KLOS!

Madison turned to the jock. "Introduce me after the next record and then get lost for an hour."

" . . . This is J.J. Jayjay on KLOS. Right now I'm gonna get in the wind for an hour or so to let my main man, Toke Madison, move on in with a special surprise for you beautiful people. Toke?"

"Thank you, J.J.," Madison said into the mike. "As you know, it's always been our policy here at KLOS to bring you not only the best of the new music, but to bring it to you before anybody else in Los Angeles. With that in mind, I want you to get on the phone and call your friends to tell them if they want to hear *Get Back,* the brand-new Beatles album, they'd better tune in right now . . .

"Are you ready, Los Angeles? Here it is, exclusively on KLOS, *the Beatles!*"

As the needle moved into the first groove on side one of the test pressing, Madison turned the monitors up in the studio.

"I want to hear this myself," he told Number. George Harrison's "Disco Jesus" filled the room:

> It's Saturday night
> And I'm really bored
> Can't wait till Sunday morning
> When I get to bump with the Lord.
>
> Yeah, Jesus gets down
> When it comes to boogie, he's the boss
> You oughta see him do the hustle
> Up there on that funky cross.

"That's *awful*, Ron," Madison said during "Disco Jesus."

"Yeah, that's the one bum cut, Toke, but wait'll you hear what's coming up. John wrote it. It's called 'Please Freeze Me.'"

> I wanna live forever,
> Don't wanna die like everyone else
> So when my time comes
> Please freeze me
> And put me on the shelf.
>
> Maybe I'll wake up in a hundred years
> A brand-new man with brand-new fears
> In a fresh world with no cares, no prayers,
> No Sonnys, and no Chers.

After "Please Freeze Me," Madison went back on the air.

"What you just heard was 'Disco Jesus' and 'Please Freeze Me' from the new Beatles album, *Get Back*, exclusively on KLOS. Call your friends and tell them if they want to hear it, they've got to tune in to KLOS right now. And call us, too. We want to hear what you think of this unusual new Beatles album . . . Coming up now is the second of George Harrison's contributions to *Get Back*. It's called 'Bring the Captain In To Kneel (Before the Altar).'"

As the song began, Madison said *"KLOS Exclusive!"* over the intro, to prevent other stations from taping it off the broadcast.

> Sure, love will keep you together
> But one day you're gonna falter
> And on that day, Toni, you'll have to
> Bring the captain in to kneel (before the altar).
>
> So shop around, you muskrat lover
> You're steady as Gibraltar
> But Judgment Day is coming, Toni, when you'll be
> Bringing the captain in to kneel (before the altar).

Madison couldn't figure it out. Were these the same Beatles that did *Sgt. Pepper?* Maybe it was just him, he thought. He decided to take some phone calls from listeners while McCartney's "Maybe I'm Amazed, Maybe I'm Not (It's None of Your Business)" went out over the air. All Ron Number could hear was Madison's half of the conversation:

"Yes, that really is the Beatles . . . Sorry you don't like it . . . What? . . . Sure, we'll play Bad Company right after the Beatles album . . . You can't wait? . . . Well, tune back in twenty minutes . . . Bye . . . Hello, Toke Madison . . . What? . . . Say, lighten up a bit, will ya? That's the Beatles you're bad-rapping, you know? . . . Peter Frampton? . . . Okay, but you'll have to wait until we've finished with this new Beatles album . . . Hello, Toke Madison, KLOS . . . What? Listen buddy, KLOS is the *only* radio station in Los Angeles where you can hear *Get Back* . . . That's right, you can check every single station on the dial, but this is the only place you can hear *Get Back* . . . What do you mean, 'thanks for the warning'? . . . Hello, Toke Madison, KLOS . . . Yes, those are the Beatles . . . Hello, KLOS, Toke Madison here . . . You told your friends to tune us in? Good . . . What? . . . No kidding? . . . Sorry . . . Look at it this way—if they were really your friends they wouldn't stop speaking to you just for that . . . Hello, this is Toke Madison, KLOS . . . When will we be finished with the Beatles album? Soon, very soon, I assure you. In fact, go ahead and turn your radio back on. We *are* through . . ."

With that, Madison lifted the needle off John Lennon's rendition of "Almost Cut My Hair" in mid-song, and switched his microphone on:

". . . What you've been listening to is *Get Back,* the new Beatles album. In case you're wondering, it'll be in the stores on Wednesday. We're gonna continue now on KLOS with Peter Frampton. Here's the most-requested cut from *Frampton '79,* called 'I'm In You, But You're In Connecticut'. . . ."

Madison wheeled around in his chair, grabbed the

Beatles album off the left-hand turntable, jammed it into its white sleeve, and threw it at Number.

"Get that piece of shit out of this building before I lose the rest of my audience!" he screamed. "That's the worst excuse for music I ever heard in my life! And do me a favor, Ron. The next time you've got an exclusive, take it over to KMET [KLOS's main competitor] so maybe I can get some of my listeners back from them."

On the morning of June 5, there was a line of over two hundred people waiting in front of the Peaches record store in Atlanta, Georgia. The minute the doors opened, a human stampede raced toward the new Beatles album.

"I never saw anything like it," Peaches owner Max Marcup told friends that night at a local bar. "This morning, hundreds of people burst in the store like we're giving records away, and this afternoon the very same people are back, but now they're demanding refunds! Of course, we don't give refunds on albums which have already been played. My mistake was telling them they could trade *Get Back* in for a $3 credit toward the price of anything else in the store. They were trading it in for roach clips, old Al Stewart albums, Farrah Fawcett posters, anything, just to get rid of it. So now I'm stuck with hundreds of used copies of *Get Back,* not to mention the thousands of new ones which I'll never move."

29

Tomorrow Never Knows

It was the most explosive Fourth of July Lee Eastman could ever remember. The Beatles' summer tour had just blown up in his face. The bomb was delivered in the form of the following telegram from Hyram Price, the nationally known concert promoter based in San Francisco:

> SINCE YOU HAVE REPEATEDLY IGNORED THE PROBLEMS SHARED BY MYSELF AND THE TWENTY-FIVE OTHER PROMOTERS ON THE TOUR, WE DECIDED AMONG OURSELVES TO TAKE ACTION. YOU WILL BE RECEIVING IN THE MAIL TOMORROW OUR SIGNED AGREEMENT TO CANCEL OUR INDIVIDUAL BEATLE CONCERTS UNLESS YOU AGREE TO OUR DEMAND OF INCLUDING ANOTHER ACT ON THE TOUR, SO THAT WE CAN SELL SUFFICIENT TICKETS TO AVOID THE HUGE FINANCIAL LOSS THAT IS GUARANTEED AT THIS POINT. I AWAIT YOUR RESPONSE.
>
> > HY PRICE
> > CONCERTS, INC.
> > SAN FRANCISCO, CALIF.

Even though both the Byrds' and the Mamas & Papas' reunion albums were disasters in the early '70s, nobody—inside or outside the record industry—expected the Beatles to meet with the same fate. As was the case with their individual solo careers, *Get Back* was a matter of too-

Beatles: They Should Have Known Better

Get Back
The Beatles
Columbia PC 39999

Kent Wright

THE BEATLES ARE back. And I think we all wish they'd stayed away.

To comprehend the magnitude of the tragedy that is *Get Back*, we must first sound the depths of the depression and disillusion establishing the ambience of the late 70's. The decade that began so pregnant with hope—peace at last, the restructuring of sexual priorities, the ultimate fulfillment of the individual—has long since turned barren, as the neo-Puritan revival, the Surinam war, and the ever-mounting shortages choke off the last vestiges of consciousness from the early 70's cultural awakening. All the while, our music followed the same despondent descent—Bowie dead, Mitchell a Park Avenue socialite, Simon occupying his seat on the Stock Exchange, with only Frampton, Scaggs and the renascent Peter Noone left to carry the experiential torch of the 70's.

We needed the Beatles back. When The Beatles died as an entity, the 60's died with them. At every crucial juncture in that crucial decade, The Beatles spoke to us, confirming what we knew to be true in our innermost hearts—first the celebration of our youthful exuberance ("She Loves You," "I Want To Hold Your Hand," "I Feel Fine,"), then simultaneously articulating and quelling our incipient doubts ("Help," "It's Only Love," "Mr. Kite"), and finally directing our idealistic movement with pithy, surefooted grace ("All You Need Is Love," "Revolution," "Let It Be," "Max-

"The Beatles are back. And I think we all wish they'd stayed away..."

Rolling Stone pans *Get Back*, June 19, 1979.

> # "A final love letter to the Beatles: Get Back to where you belong—to our hopes and dreams and our memories. May they rest in pieces..."

well's Silver Hammer"). Without The Beatles, the 70's soldiered bravely onward for a space and a time, but their return was long overdue. Oh, how we needed The Beatles back.

We needed a great Beatles album. We needed it more than we knew, needed it to crystallize and focus our long-suppressed rage so long diffused in vague, inarticulate frustration, needed it to point the way upward from our seemingly infinite vortex of cynicism and despair. We needed The Beatles to give us hope anew. And they blew it.

Instead of exorcising our demons for us, The Beatles placate, even pander to them. The rampant cynicism of "Maybe I'm Amazed, Maybe I'm Not (It's None Of Your Business)", caustic as a Brechtian libretto though it is, is in the last analysis appalling empty, devoid of the essential sympathy informing earlier monuments like "Glass Onion" and "Nowhere Man." John's "Please Freeze Me," at first appears to offer a clever cryogenic escape route:

I wanna live forever
Don't wanna die like everyone else
So when my time comes
Please freeze me
And put me on the shelf

But by the time the song's protagonist is awakened, "a brand new man with brand new fears/ In a fresh world with no cares, no prayers, no Sonny's and no Chers," the listener is overwhelmed with the bitter realization that the future road this

global village will travel is doomed to be an even bleaker street than the one down which we currently plod.

The sense of enervating ennui pervading the album is not lightened by the trivial pie-in-the-sky Pollyanna panegyrics of "Hold On To A Dream." That sort of simplistic cant was suitable for "Can't Buy Me Love" and other songs of an ineluctably more naive era, but rings falsely hollow today, especially when followed by "Yoko's Going Broke-o," a pointlessly spiteful diatribe against the Philistinism of America's major art dealers and museums (surely this target was forever skewered by the brilliant social satirist Harry Chapin in last year's penetrating "Painting By The Numbers").

Similarly, the *intent* of "Gilligan's Island" is clearly inspirational in tone, but the actual *perception* has just as clearly gone awry:

Bob Denver, Jim Backus
Each day they attack us
With laughter, fun and truth

It is difficult to imagine what possessed the once-insightful Lennon & McCartney (this is the team that wrote "Mean Mr. Mustard," damn it!) to focus on such a woefully inane mass-entertainment shuck as "Gilligan's Island" as a wellspring of hope, particularly when most informed observers would agree that an infinitely more suitable source follows immediately afterward in most

major metropolitan television markets. I speak, of course, of "Leave It To Beaver."

As for George Harrison's two compositions, "Disco Jesus" and "Bring The Captain In To Kneel (At The Altar)," the less said the better. Harrison's own reservoir of spiritual creativity has obviously long since dried up, but after masterful distillations of the religious rock of ages like "My Sweet Lord," "Ding Dong," and "Crackerbox Palace," it's at least understandable that the vein has been exhausted. It's Lennon & McCartney's artistic failure that is at issue here, and somehow it comes as the supreme irony to discover that on this hollow facade of an album only "Almost Cut My Hair," written by David Crosby almost a decade ago, expresses any semblance of the essential defiance and pride with which The Beatles originally inspired a generation. David Crosby, according to reliable reports, has recently been reduced to driving an old Rambler to state fairs and carnivals, showing slides of his past career highlights. It is indeed a pitiful new kind of Crosby, Stills & Nash, but in his own senile way David Crosby's fidelity to the muse of rock & roll is greater than that of the once-illustrious Beatles. Better they allowed us to cherish our reminiscences of the glorious Fab Four of yore than tarnished them with such a hopeless sham. A final love letter to The Beatles: Get back where you belong—to our hopes and dreams, and our *memories.* May they rest in pieces.

much-expected and too-little-delivered, a lethal combination that resulted in millions of album returns to Columbia and a pronounced lack of interest in the Beatles' upcoming tour. The album was universally panned in every publication from *Rolling Stone* to *Women's Wear Daily*. The reviews were vicious, written with the kind of venom that one expects only from someone who has been betrayed, cheated, lied to, or ripped off. But that's exactly the way *Get Back* was received, as a betrayal of everything that Beatles fans had dreamed of for ten years. They expected magic, and all they got was music. Of the Beatles, John Lennon took the failure the hardest.

"I *knew* those songs weren't as good as they should have been," he told McCartney during a break in the rehearsal for the tour. "We had no business putting out that album, tour or no tour."

McCartney defended it: "Those were the best songs we were capable of writing, John. We both know that."

"Maybe so," Lennon conceded, recalling the difficulty of writing anything for *Get Back*, "but I guess I'm still not used to criticism, at least not the amount we've taken for this album."

"Don't you remember our agreement at your house a few months ago? Fuck the public, that's what we said. We were going to write to get ourselves off. You told me you were *hungry* to create, so we created. Why must you look at *Get Back* as a failure? Why not view it as a meal for your mind?"

"Maybe you're right, Paul. Can you excuse me for a minute?"

"Sure. Where are you going?"

"To the bathroom. My mind has to throw up."

Eastman's back was against the wall and he knew it as he made the transatlantic call to London to Ken Percent, manager of several of England's biggest acts, including Peter Frampton.

Columbia Records' advertising department
goes back to Beatles' first album in headline for *Get
Back* album ad.

"Hello, Ken, this is Lee Eastman of Beatles, Incorporated. How are you?"

"Rich. What can I do for you, Mr. Eastman?"

"Are you aware of the Beatles' American tour?"

"I certainly am. In fact, I'll be in Los Angeles the night they play there and I'm having a devil of a time trying to give my tickets away."

"Ha, ha, ha. Listen, Ken—what I'm about to offer you is the chance of a lifetime."

"Go ahead. It'll be my fifth chance of a lifetime this week."

"I want Peter Frampton as opening act for the entire Beatles tour—Ken? Ken? Hello? Hello? . . ."

Eastman was talking to a dial tone. He called back.

"Hello, Ken? I'm sorry. Afraid we got disconnected. Either that or you hung up on me, ha, ha—"

"I did hang up on you, Eastman. I'm a busy man. I can't have people wasting my time."

"Am I to believe you aren't interested in joining a Beatles tour?"

"I couldn't have said it better. Only ruder."

"But . . . if I may ask . . . why?"

"Because—and I'm only going to say this once, so please pay attention—you want the hottest act in show business to open up for your group of tired, washed-up old troubadours. What do we have to profit from such an association? As a matter of fact, you'd have a big job on your hands just convincing me to let the Beatles *open* for Peter Frampton . . ."

Eastman made a desperation move.

"How big a job, Ken?"

"You're willing to have the Beatles play second-billed to Frampton?"

"Well, suppose we share the billing?"

"Out of the question. Absolutely not. The only thing I would even consider is top billing."

"But we're talking about the Beatles, Ken."

"Talk about the Beatles all day, Eastman, but it's Frampton who's going to sell the tickets, so it's Frampton who gets top billing."

Eastman hated to do it, but he knew there was no other way out. As for Ken Percent, he found great satisfaction in the idea of his act being billed over the greatest institution in music history.

"Okay, Ken. You've got your top billing. How about it?"

"One condition."

"What?"

"I just signed another group, the Sex Pistols. I want them on the tour as well. They need the American exposure."

"Are those the same Sex Pistols who wear safety pins in their ears and shout obscenities at the audience during their songs?"

"Don't be running down the Sex Pistols, Eastman. They're fine, exuberant young lads who only express the good-natured rebellion which is part of the growing-up process. Also, I own ten percent of them."

"Just don't ask me to bill them over the Beatles."

"Eastman, I'm genuinely amazed, and a little hurt, too. What do you take me for? Some sort of greedy, pushy manager-type? I'm willing to have the Pistols share second billing with your group."

"Share?" an angry Eastman screamed into the receiver. "Either the Sex Pistols go on before the Beatles, or the deal's off."

"You drive a hard bargain, Eastman, but okay, you win. The Sex Pistols, the Beatles, then Frampton to close the show. Will that be an acceptable billing?"

"Do I have a choice?" a weary Eastman asked.

"Certainly. There's bankruptcy, humiliation, suicide . . . you've got plenty of choices. While you're making up your mind, please have your accountants get in touch with me so we can make all the necessary financial arrangements. Good day, Mr. Eastman."

A vote was taken and John Lennon was elected to inform Lee Eastman that the Beatles weren't about to be second-billed to anyone.

"We're all plenty pissed, Lee," Lennon said in Eastman's office. "You didn't even bother to ask us—"

"There was no time, John. Frampton's manager was insistent."

"I don't care about Frampton's manager and I don't care about Frampton, either. How can you expect us to be opening act for him? Or for anybody? We're the goddamn Beatles for chrissakes! We close the fucking show!"

"You want to close a show that nobody is attending?" Eastman asked.

"I know sales are slow, we all know it. But you'd better fucking believe we'd rather work to a half-full house than to suffer the humiliation of opening for someone else!"

"John, without Frampton those stadiums won't be even one-fourth filled."

"I don't care! We're the headliners or no tour! That's final!"

"Are you aware of what 'no tour' means?" Eastman inquired. "You back out and they'll sue us for every penny we've got. And if we go without Frampton, it'll be just as bad. Remember what I told you about how our payment on this tour was in commission?"

"Sure. I remember. Ninety percent."

"Well, those promoters are going to get their cut first. They've got to pay for the stadium rental, for the promotion, for the tickets. By ourselves, we won't even generate enough dollars for them to meet their expenses."

"So we work for free, then. I hate to do it, but we can afford it."

"It's not a matter of working for free, John. Do you

An ad from the *Los Angeles Times* "Calendar" section, July 15, 1979.

realize the kind of overhead we've got? It's a matter of working at a loss—a big loss—at every stop on the tour. It's going to wipe us out."

"Wipe us out? You mean break us?"

"That's what I've been trying to tell you."

"I guess there's no choice, then. I certainly don't want to end up like Mickey Rooney."

"I wouldn't worry about that, John," Eastman reassured him. "Even if you did go bankrupt, it wouldn't make you any shorter."

Eastman immediately set the necessary changes in motion. He contacted the tour's twenty-six promoters and told them they could expect to receive entirely new promotional packages, including posters and programs featuring Frampton as headliner.[1] Extensive travel accommodations had to be hurriedly set up for both the Frampton and Sex Pistols entourages. As the promoters expected, ticket sales immediately skyrocketed with the addition of Frampton, and the tour was assured of financial success.

Johnny Rotten, lead singer of the Sex Pistols, had taken all the abuse he was going to take from the 50,000 people who jammed Dodger Stadium on opening night of the Peter Frampton tour. For Rotten, the firecracker thrown onstage during their "Anarchy in the U.K." was the final straw. He signaled his band to stop in the middle of the song, then, taking the microphone with him, jumped off the nine-foot stage (which was located where second base would be at a baseball game). Dodging the barrage of fruit and seat cushions aimed at him, he strode around the infield, issuing a demand to the crowd:

1. A few of the discarded original posters and programs (which featured an artist's rendition of the Beatles in an antique airplane flying over a "Mt. Rushmore" likeness of themselves) have recently surfaced. These are worth a fortune in today's collectors' marketplace.

"I WANT THE GUTLESS VACANT NOSEFUCKER WHO THREW THAT FIRECRACKER TO COME DOWN HERE AND IDENTIFY HIMSELF. COME ON, YOU MINDLESS ..."

The crowd began chanting *"WE WANT FRAMPTON, WE WANT FRAMPTON ..."* But Johnny Rotten wasn't ready to hand over the mike.

"YOU'LL GET PETER FRAMPTON, ALL RIGHT. YOU'LL GET HIM. YOU IDIOTS DESERVE HIM! BUT FIRST, YOU'LL HAVE TO SIT THROUGH THAT BUNCH OF EXILES FROM THE OLD-AGE HOME, THE BEATLES. I HEARD THOSE OLD FARTS AT REHEARSAL THIS AFTERNOON AND THEY BORED THE SHIT OUT OF ME. BUT SINCE ALL FIFTY THOUSAND OF YOU BORE THE SHIT OUT OF ME, TOO, YOU'LL PROBABLY LIKE THEM—"

At this point, several uniformed security guards descended on Rotten, one of whom grabbed the microphone out of his hand, leaving the obviously terrified guard with an open mike and an audience of 50,000:

"I'VE BEEN ASKED TO INFORM YOU THAT AFTER A BREAK OF ABOUT A HALF-HOUR OR SO, THE SHOW WILL RESUME WITH ... UH ... WITH ... WHAT'S THE NAME OF THE NEXT BAND? ... WHAT? ... THE NEEDLES? ... OH, RIGHT! ... COMING UP NEXT IS THE BEATLES!"

George Harrison was sipping a Coke as he leaned against a wall in the dressing room during the break. John Lennon walked in, his Rickenbacker guitar preceding him.

"Nervous?" Harrison asked.

"Yeah. A little. You?"

"Naah. I have a little ritual for times like these. I meditate. Just finished, in fact."

"I have a ritual myself," Lennon informed him. "I get sick. Just finished, in fact."

"Where's Paul?" Harrison asked.

"I just passed him in the hall. He was surrounded by a couple dozen females."

Harrison looked relieved. "Well, at least it's good to know we've got some fans left."

McCartney entered the room furiously. He spotted a baseball locker and slammed his fist into it.

"What's eating you?" Harrison asked. "John just told me you were being mauled by a bunch of female fans."

"Oh, they were fans all right," McCartney said in a voice mixed with anger and hurt. "But they weren't fans of ours. They were bloody Peter Frampton fans!"

"Oh," Harrison said. He understood. Since the day Paul joined the Beatles, he'd always been the one the girls went for. Paul had been a Teen Idol most of his life, and now his turn was over.

McCartney was still steaming, "You should have heard them!" He began affecting the voice of a thirteen-year-old girl: " 'Where's Peter?' 'What's Peter really like?' 'Will you give this note to Peter?' 'What does Peter's girlfriend look like?' "

"For God's sake, Paul," Lennon said, "you had *your* day as teenybopper fave. Let Frampton have his. You should be glad there's not going to be any of that on this tour."

A pretty preteen girl wandered into the dressing room. When she caught sight of Lennon, Harrison and McCartney, her eyes opened until they were the size of quarters.

"Aren't you the Bea . . . the Beat . . ."

Lennon laughed. This cute little girl was so terrified.

"Yes, sweetheart," he said. "It's us. We're the Beatles."

"My God! The Beatles! You're actually the Beatles?"

"Yes," Lennon said again.

"Then you must know Peter Frampton! I'd give anything if you'd introduce me—"

That was as far as she got before Lennon exploded:

"GET OUT OF HERE! GET THE HELL OUT OF HERE! NOW! I MEAN RIGHT NOW!"

"For God's sake, John," Paul said. "You had your day as teenybopper fave. Let Frampton have his."

"I'll let you have yours in a minute," Lennon threatened, but Ringo entered with the news that they were due onstage in two minutes.

Ringo clutched his drumsticks, Lennon his Rickenbacker guitar, Harrison his Gretsch Tennessean, and McCartney his Hofner bass, as the four stood in the Los Angeles Dodgers' dugout listening to disc jockey Wolfman Jack's introduction:

"THIS NEXT GROUP IS THE ONE THAT PETER FRAMPTON CREDITS AS BEING HIS BIGGEST INFLUENCE. IT WAS FROM THEIR RECORDS THAT PETER LEARNED TO PLAY GUITAR. I'M SURE YOU ALL REMEMBER THEIR MANY HITS, INCLUDING 'SHE LOVES YOU,' 'I WANNA HOLD YOUR HAND,' AND ALL THE REST, SO NOW LET'S GIVE A BIG LOS ANGELES WELCOME TO—IN THEIR FIRST PERFORMANCE IN THIRTEEN YEARS—THE BEATLES!"

One at a time, they emerged from the dugout, just as they had emerged from this same dugout almost thirteen years earlier to the day. In 1966 the exuberant Beatles ran at full speed toward the stage, but the 1979 version sauntered lamely across the infield, shoulders hunched, heads down, averting a look into the vastness of the audience—someone else's audience.

As Ringo positioned himself behind the drums and watched John, Paul, and George begin tuning up, it occurred to him that thirteen years earlier, they didn't bother tuning up. The crowd made so much noise in those days, it didn't matter.

Lennon opened up his mike. "Hello, Los Angeles. It's good to be back . . ."

The word "back" was the cue for the tightly rehearsed

Beatles to launch into their opening number, "Back in the U.S.S.R." It was a strong, energetic version, but the crowd was unmoved. The Beatles appeared to be playing to a huge painting of 50,000 people. "Come Together" followed. As Harrison handled the tricky guitar solo, Lennon looked into the vast audience. Now there was movement. But something was wrong. The movement was all toward the aisle. It occurred to Lennon that the crowd was using the Beatles' set as an opportunity to go to the snack bar, to the bathroom, to meet friends—in other words, to prepare itself for Peter Frampton. Not since their earliest days when they went out as the warm–up act for touring American stars like Roy Orbison, had the Beatles experienced this particular form of indignity.

A few scattered boos were heard during Harrison's "Disco Jesus," a tune from the new album. This should have been a clue. The following three songs from *Get Back* were each received with barely a smattering of applause.

"We're dying out here," Lennon whispered into McCartney's ear as the set progressed.

"I know, I know," McCartney whispered back. "But the oldies are coming up. If that doesn't do it, nothing will."

McCartney didn't know how right he was. For as soon as Ringo began the drum roll that opened "She Loves You," the audience came alive for the first time that night. The medley continued with "From Me to You," "I Saw Her Standing There," "Twist and Shout," and "Can't Buy Me Love." They closed the show with the first song they ever played in America—fifteen years earlier on the "Ed Sullivan Show"—"All My Loving."

When the Beatles left the stage, 50,000 people cheered them back on. It was a confusing moment for Lennon. He began the encore number, "I Want to Hold Your Hand," with decidedly mixed feelings.

While it felt good to have finally reached this huge audience, the songs that broke the ice were songs he hated. They embarrassed him, these oldies. What was he—a forty-year-old adult—doing before 50,000 people singing about holding hands?

As he and McCartney held the song's last word, "hand," through the required seven beats that signaled a final Harrison chord, the crowd went crazy. A huge makeshift banner unraveled in the second deck, proclaiming "BEATLES FOREVER!!!"

McCartney held his guitar high over his head amidst the screaming as he led the Beatles across the infield and into the dugout. Inside the locker room a case of Coors, delivered during the performance, was attacked with a vengeance. For five minutes they drank in silence. Lee Eastman stood outside the door, turning groupies and well-wishers away.

McCartney spoke first. "All's well that ends well, I guess."

"It was a big finish, all right," Ringo added.

"It got a little scary out there for a while," George said. "I could have been singing in a different language for all the response I was getting."

"Bill Haley" Lennon said.

"What?" McCartney asked.

"It was Bill Haley out there," Lennon repeated. "That's exactly what it was and you all know it but you won't admit it."

"What do you mean, 'Bill Haley'?" Ringo asked.

"Bill Haley!" It was so obvious, Lennon thought. Why couldn't they see it? "We were Bill Haley."

"Why?" McCartney asked. "Because we did a few oldies that makes us into Bill Haley?"

"No, that's not it," Lennon explained. "You don't understand. Look, when I was singing 'She Loves You' out there and 'I Wanna Hold Your Hand' and those others, I had this weird feeling, like what Bill Haley must have felt the last twenty-five years singing 'Rock Around the Clock.' He's got to hate that song even more than I hate 'She

Loves You' but he's in the same boat as us. He's a prisoner of his past."

"It's not the same thing," McCartney insisted. "We won't be singing those oldies every night for the rest of our lives. They're crowd-pleasers, that's all. What's so bad about pleasing the crowd?"

"You're not listening to me, Paul. It's not the idea of singing oldies that bothers me, it's the fact that it's all they wanted to hear. They don't give a shit about our recent songs, and God knows they've got no use for our new album."

Eastman entered the room. "I've got some bad news," he said. Then, noticing the four glum faces in front of him, he added, "It can wait until tomorrow if you aren't in the mood for it."

"Go ahead, Lee," George said. "Can't make me any more depressed than John's been making me."

"Okay. I talked to Lee Soption from Columbia tonight. He said he wasn't supposed to say anything about it for a couple weeks, but he figured the sooner we knew, the better off we'd be . . ."

"Knew what?" John asked.

"They aren't picking up our option," Eastman said. "They've dropped us from the label."

At that moment, the entire room began to shake violently. All four Beatles dived under a long bench in the locker room, certain it was an earthquake. Eastman bolted out the door into the hall. He returned seconds later.

"Relax, fellows. It's nothing. Peter Frampton just went on, that's all. The place went berserk."

One by one, the Beatles slowly picked themselves up off the cold cement floor.

"As soon as the tour's over, I'll set up another deal for us. Don't worry," Eastman promised and left the room again to resume his post outside the locker room door.

The Beatles were despondent, especially Lennon.

"So here we are," he said. "No label, no future, nothing but a great past. That's all we've got to look forward to: the past."

"What I don't get," Ringo said, "is all that noise about a Beatles reunion. For ten bloody years, that's all I heard. Not one day went by without somebody asking me when we'd get back together."

"What don't you understand?" McCartney asked.

"Just this. If they wanted us to get back together so badly, why didn't they support us?"

"They never really did want *us* to come back, Ringo," John said. "We were just symbols of the things they did want back—their youth, their innocence—"

"The sixties," Ringo added.

"Right," Lennon continued. "That's all we mean to them. They only want us when we remind them of the good old days. As long as we sing 'She Loves You,' everything's all right. For three minutes, they're back in high school in the sixties when they had no responsibilities, no worries, no obligations."

"Just like when Bill Haley sings 'Rock Around the Clock' for his generation," McCartney said slowly.

"See? That's exactly what I meant," Lennon said.

"It's funny, isn't it?" Harrison added. "All those reviews about how we betrayed our audience, yet we're the ones who were really betrayed. They beg us to come back, then they lock us into the past."

"It's not their fault." McCartney said. "Think about it. If you went to see Bill Haley, what would you want to hear? His new songs? No way."

McCartney made his point. It led to a brief conversation, after which Eastman was called back into the room. His daughter Linda was with him.

"Don't set up another record deal for us, Lee," McCartney said. "We'll finish the tour, but that's it. There's no more Beatles after that."

Eastman was stunned. "But . . . why?"

"I guess," McCartney said as he took his wife's hand, "it's because you can't live in someone's past and live in their future, too."

Paul and Linda walked out the door, followed by Ringo, George, and John. They climbed into a waiting limousine and drove off into the Los Angeles night.

ACKNOWLEDGMENTS

I want to express my gratitude to the many friends who helped with *Paperback Writer*.

Thanks to Michael Ochs and Jean Radnetter for their photos, and to Steve Uslan, Roger Zumwalt, Bob Baker, and Michael Barackman for their assistance.

Special thanks to Marty Cerf at *Phonograph Record Magazine* for affording me the creative freedom that led to this book; to Richard Zumwalt, for his insight during the early stages of the project which helped shape the original manuscript; and to Paula Einstein, for graciously lending her time and wit to the editing of the current edition.

Above all, to Dave Hirsch and Ken Barnes for giving so much, to Bob Wilson for making it all possible, to Fred Jordan for believing, and to Russell Barnard—the best adviser, editor, and friend anyone could ask for.

And thanks to John, George, Paul and Ringo for the excitement and magic that was the Beatles.

—Mark Shipper

Credits

Photos

Pages 25, 33, 53, 57, 81—Capitol Publicity
Page 6, 118 (*Sgt. Pepper* LP), and back cover—Jean Radnetter
Page 55—Martin Cerf/*Phonograph Record Magazine*
All other photos—Michael Ochs Archives

Illustrations

Page 191—from Creem Magazine, June 1974 and June 1975 issues.

All other magazine and/or newspaper articles illustrated herein, including *Rolling Stone, Time, Los Angeles Times, Dallas Morning News,* etc. are fictitious and did not actually appear in their respective publications. All quotes from these and other publications are not authentic. All Capitol and Apple albums shown are fictitious.

Page 236-7—The *Rolling Stone* review of *Get Back* was written by Ken Barnes (who also claims worldwide rights to the name of photographer F. Stop Fitzgerald).

Page 95—From a suggestion by Dave Hirsch.

All other illustrations designed by Mark Shipper.

1. Roy Carr and Tony Tyler's excellent *The Beatles—An Illustrated Record* (Harmony Books, New York) was an invaluable research source throughout. I highly recommend it to anyone with an interest in the Beatles.